I'm Not Like Everybody Else

I'm Not Like Everybody Else

A collection of Manchester-inspired
short stories and poems for outsiders,
misfits and rebels

Richard Dalgety

Matador
9 Priory Business Park,
Wistow Road, Kibworth Beauchamp,
Leicestershire. LE8 0RX
Tel: 0116 279 2299
Email: books@troubador.co.uk
Web: www.troubador.co.uk/matador
Twitter: @matadorbooks

ISBN 978 1788035 118

British Library Cataloguing in Publication Data.
A catalogue record for this book is available from the British Library.

Printed and bound in the UK by TJ International, Padstow, Cornwall
Typeset in 11pt Minion Pro by Troubador Publishing Ltd, Leicester, UK

Matador is an imprint of Troubador Publishing Ltd

There is nothing to writing. All you do is sit down at a typewriter and bleed

Ernest Hemingway

If you want to know who your friends are, get yourself a jail sentence

Charles Bukowski

CONTENTS

Poems

AUTHOR'S FOREWORD

In 2004 I wrote a collection of short stories titled *I Wasn't Made For These Times* before a career in the charity sector started consuming the majority of my time. These stories were focused on characters that society had forgotten about – outsiders, misfits, outlaws – and the stories aimed to bring these characters to life. *I'm Not Like Everybody Else* is a follow up to *I Wasn't Made For These Times* and is named after the great Ray Davies-penned Kinks B-side to 'Sunny Afternoon', a song that topped the British singles charts in the month that the England football team won the World Cup. I wanted the stories and poems in this collection to have a Manchester theme and to explore the dilemmas of principlism against pragmatism for characters that would be considered outsiders by many in society – murderers, rejects, the falsely accused, psychopaths, religiously obsessed loners, cross-dressers.....

In 2016, with more time on my hands than I knew how to handle and raging at the injustices and frustrations of my own life as an outsider at the time, I sat in Salford and Manchester pubs and wrote and wrote and wrote.......

IN TIMES OF TURMOIL

*In the depth of winter, I finally learned that within me
there lay an invincible summer*

Albert Camus

In times of turmoil find a home to attack from.

I write best when I am uptight, taut and emotional. I write best when I am on the brink of a breakdown.

I murdered my wife earlier this year. I am pretty sure I did, although I have been on the run for so long that everything has become one long delusional torturous nightmare. Like a Frank Zappa guitar solo, you want it to end, because the reality is hellish and freakish, but you don't want it to end because the pain is addictive and the alternatives are worse.

I was forty-seven years old at the time. No children; nothing remarkable about my life that would make the police, the press or you show an interest in me. Living in Swinton, Manchester. Supporting the Blues. In thrall to the glory days of Madchester and the Stone Roses. Sometimes it is better not to look back in life. The wife of Lot did this and was turned into a pillar of salt. I killed my wife with a gun. She had it coming to her.

1

Being on the run from the law was the most exciting white-knuckle ride I have been on in my life. The fake passport, the false names, based on previous outlaw heroes of mine, sometimes spelt backwards, sometimes with letters jumbled up, sometimes just referencing them in more obscure ways – Jimmy Tooth, Owen Longbow, Darren Cash. I always loved the Harrison Ford character in *The Fugitive* and had watched it many times without realising I would become like him. Only difference is that I am guilty of murder – guilty as hell.

How can you make an unremarkable life exciting? Maureen had never wanted children and that ate away at me year on year. I would never be able to take a son to the football or be a protective dad for my daughter. A traditional Salford wedding. A conventional and unimaginative set of relatives. No one ever asked me how I felt. No one ever talked about love. No one ever talked about what we are talking about now – to anyone.

Maureen was never physically unfaithful, I don't think, and neither was I. However, her apathy and her lack of adventure and spontaneity turned the bedroom cold and turned me into a shell of the man I could have been.

'We are too old to go to gigs, Joe!'

'It's not the 1990s anymore. Grow up and stop being Peter Pan.'

'I am voting Conservative. Too many immigrants coming over here and taking our jobs.'

'You know I don't want kids, Joe. I have stated that all along.'

'You need to drink less. How are we going to afford

the work doing on the garden if you are in the pub every weekend?'

There was no Cleopatra's Needle. There was only the art of war. Little by little, month on month, year on year, I trained my mind into becoming a psychopath. I am not actually a psychopath, but I made myself become like one. The night terror would grip me, the white heat of the plan. I wanted to recapture all those seasons in the sun that were there in my head, not reached yet, but achievable in some way… maybe. To walk along a beach like Andy Dufresne and know that you had escaped your past and you could start your life all over again.

To have just one buddy that believes in you, to have just one home you can attack from, to have freedom in your mind and spirit. I am almost there now.

I am driving through Utah in a Mustang with Iggy and the Stooges' *Raw Power* album in the CD player. The only proof I need for the existence of God is music.

Around me is a scene of great desolation. I can drive faster and faster. I can turn the music up louder and louder. Nobody can touch me now. The open road is my home. Only when I sleep do I feel afraid. I can't get to sleep. When I do I get two hours and then I wake up thinking I am in a dream. Then I wake up properly and know that I am living this. The first few hours of the day in solitude are horrible. Only when I get the car wheels rolling and the music up loud do I get the feeling I want to feel. Like Kerouac said, the road is life. It is the only place I am free, the only place I feel happy. No one knows me on the road – I have the total and blissful anonymity that I never had with my wife in Manchester. I have found an escape from my dark and lonely place. In a dark and lonely place. In a dark and lonely place. In a dark and lonely place.

A man who has never fallen has never stood up.

A man who fell down a long time ago tried to stand up.

I killed her and I know it. Just to watch her die, I guess.

The night it happened I came home late from a session down The Legion. I had picked the date for spiritual reasons. I had known for sure that she would be asleep and that there would be no one else around. Drinking with Chad and Billy, discussing the game, discussing Pep Guardiola and his possible genius. Chad had even got his hair cut to look like Pep. Lots of arguments about the summer signings and what Mourinho was up to on the other side of the city:

'In France, they have an expression for getting battered, Joe. They call it "getting *Zlataned*".'

'The highlight of my summer was seeing the Roses at the Emirates. Ian Brown owned the place that night.'

'You OK tonight, Joe? You look tense. Taut, uptight, emotional. Here, sink one of these, it'll help you relax.'

Chad left early and Billy and I enjoyed a lock-in of sorts. A few shots flowed and Billy did more of the talking. Pep Guardiola and the Stone Roses. Jesus, he sounded like a broken record. I left abruptly. He seemed upset at this. In a dark and lonely place.

In a dark and lonely place I entered my own peaceful house around 1am. The house of eighteen years of stultifying and suffocating marriage. This was not the home to attack from. This was the other end of the spectrum from the thrills of an American highway.

4

I shot her in the back of the head around 1:20am, trembling and hesitating for around thirty seconds in the autumn cold and silence. I took the gun with me and a bag of clothes and things I cared about. I got in the car and drove fast, but not too fast that it would draw attention to me. I had the fake passport in my jeans all night (I nearly pulled it out by mistake in the pub earlier on). Straight to Liverpool John Lennon Airport and then a series of planes that ought to confuse everyone. Once I had hired a car, grown a beard and dismantled my entire fucking brain and memory I had left my dark and lonely place.

So months later I am here driving south and knowing I will get caught one day. But I want to get my kicks every day now and that in itself is worth being alive for. There is no guilt. There is no fear. There is just an adrenaline rush and a newfound self-confidence that means I have lived a good life. I have got the freedom and excitement that I had always wanted all those eighteen years. The years before that were nothing special either; just a regular guy trying to fit in and not knowing his identity or place in the world.

I have an identity now. I am an outlaw. I am on the run. I am a killer on the loose and I feel fine about it. I am a psychopath, without a conscience and without pity and shame. I admired the Nicaraguan Sandinistas because they didn't sit back and let bad things happen; they were proactive and took action.

Driving down the highway, faster and faster, tune after glorious tune. Spontaneous music and spontaneous driving leading to spontaneous actions. Maureen's gone. My old life is gone.

Then I hear the state trooper's siren and I see them in my rear-view mirror. Three cars. Lights flashing. Can I outrun them? There isn't much gas left in the tank. The music is loud and aggressive, but the sirens are turning it into a cacophony. I put my foot to the floor for one last adrenaline rush, one last golden thrill to beat all thrills. It lasts and lasts and lasts. The lead singer is singing for me. The drums propel me forward. Make me feel like I am Icarus. Then suddenly and jerkily I take my foot off the gas and throw myself back in my seat. The game is up and I know I can't escape now.

I want to kill myself. I want to do it myself without any assistance. I don't want anyone else to do it for me.

In a dark and lonely place, I believe in free will.

In a dark and lonely place that I will never return from.

THE BALLAD OF THE SEPTEMBER MAN

Talent is a long patience. The September Man told me that and it has always stuck in my brain. There is a part of everything which is unexplored, because we are accustomed to using our eyes only in association with the memory of what people before us have thought of the thing we are looking at. Even the smallest thing has something in it which is unknown. We must find it.

The September Man has upset my hope, my art, my fantasy. He has destroyed my aspirations, ravaged my confidence, killed my love, murdered the illusions of the heart, and altogether performed the most gigantic sceptical operation that I have ever seen carried out. He has riddled everything with his mockery, drained everything dry.

September where I come from has always been a curious month. I become a year older every year and have to adjust my world view accordingly. It is the start of every academic year and the end of every summer and the hopes and dreams that each summer holds. Yet sometimes in the Indian summer moments there are memories greater and more poignant than the false promises of the 'hottest summer since 1976' and the disappointments of our nation's sporting teams and anti-heroes.

I like to walk down by the River Irwell at this time of year, maybe after a pint in that symbol of truth, the King's Arms in Salford or the Rovers Return on Chapel Street. The best September days can have great blue expanses of sky outside my window. You know you have to cherish it, because you weren't expecting it and once this day has gone you might not see something like it again until April.

As I walked down by the River Irwell I saw happy couples passing and birds singing. I saw the river flow elegantly beside me and around me was the bustle of bearded young men and pristine and immaculate women. Like a character in a Lowry painting, I felt I was part of something big, something with historical importance. The passers-by all seemed to be smiling at me today. Summer had returned, the light was warm and bright, and happiness was in the air.

I sat on a bench for a while and a young girl came and sat next to me. I would guess that she was in her early twenties and dressed as though she was working in an office nearby. She had golden hair, a retro haircut and a natural beauty that was likely to inspire young men in rock and roll bands. In the breeze her long hair rippled down to her ears and the nape of her neck. I felt an irresistible longing to kiss her.

I stared at her so intently that she turned her head towards me and suddenly lowered her eyes. She smiled and revealed an unaffected innocence as I turned away and tried to seem unaware of the chemistry between us.

I felt a longing to start a conversation, but I hesitated and started running future scenarios through my head. Was this my future wife? Was this 'the one'?

I was just about to speak to her when the September Man touched me on my shoulder. He was sat further up the bench and was older than me. I imagined him to be in his forties. He was handsome, but looked jaded and had a weariness and a gravelly voice that immediately drew my attention away from the girl.

'I think I need to have a word with you,' the September Man said.

'Sorry, do I know you?' I responded.

'What I am going to tell you now is very important.'

I stood up and walked with him over to the bridge across the River Irwell and we started talking more intensely as we leant over the railings with the murky river gushing below us.

'When your doctor tells you to eat certain things or avoid eating or drinking certain things, you will do it. When he prescribes certain antibiotics you will take them until they have run their course. In the same way I am saying to you now, beware of that girl! I saw you falling for her then and I have come to rescue you at just the right moment, just at the moment when you will still listen without prejudice to my advice. Beware of that girl with golden hair. All of her snares are set. All of her weapons are sharpened. All of her treacherous wiles are prepared. Beware of love! It is more dangerous than all colds, bronchitis or cancerous growths. It shows no mercy and it drives us all to commit irreparable acts of folly. I am acting like a government warning for you now. Like the

9

writing and photos on a cigarette packet. You can make your choice when I stop speaking. It is wrong to believe that one moment will always follow another one, in a traditional linear fashion, and that once a moment is gone it is gone forever. Like I said, you can make a choice when I stop speaking.'

The September Man put his head in his hands for a while and stopped talking. I liked him and I smiled. He seemed so genuine and I felt like a disciple. But then I looked again at the beautiful young girl sat on the bench forty yards away. She continued to eat her lunch in isolation, oblivious to the waves that she was causing around her.

'I am going to tell you a story,' continued the September Man. 'It happened around ten years ago when I was working in the Town Hall on Albert Square. It was September time and I had a longing for some sparks to give my life extra meaning and texture.

'I told my boss I was feeling ill one day and left work early to wander through the city. Oh how I wish my boss hadn't been so lenient!

'I walked around in love with the vibrancy and the people around me. It was a bright and early autumn day that was so close to perfection like this one.

'I boarded my usual bus home when all of a sudden on Oxford Road a young woman came on board carrying some shopping and sat directly opposite me and smiled deeply into my eyes. We talked instantly as if no one else was around. We discussed our days, our lives and our experiences like two people on a first date, until it came time for both of us to leave at the same stop. We continued walking together into Didsbury and she said she was going to a Belle and Sebastian concert that Friday evening with her friend. I said I loved them too and would try to get a ticket. We stood still for ten minutes more and continued talking and then we exchanged phone numbers. It was a lightning bolt moment in my life.

'We went to the concert together that Friday and we gave each other flirtatious sideways glances throughout our respective favourite songs. The following week I took her for dinner and we made love for the first time. Not long after we moved in together. She would always sing verses from *The Boy with the Arab Strap* to me, whenever she wanted to recapture the magic of those first few weeks and months together.'

As the September Man continued to talk I looked over at the girl with golden hair and I felt less captivated than before. The September Man held me in his thrall and had total control over me.

'The months passed, my friend, and the magic faded. We accommodated each other's lifestyles, let some of our respective hobbies and passions fall by the wayside. I compromised my life for her. I started seeing less of my friends, less of my family and my work suffered.

'The arguments grew and the restlessness grew. I lost my head completely and I married her because it was what society expected me to do. You imagine to yourself how happy life would be with a woman, and off you go and marry her.

'And then she calls you names from morning until night, knows nothing, understands nothing, chatters endlessly, starts singing James Blunt songs at you – Oh how I hate

James Blunt! – tells all her friends all of your domestic secrets and bedroom intimacies, and has her head stuffed with such idiotic superstitions and ludicrous opinions and such monstrous tabloid newspaper prejudices that you feel like crying yourself to sleep every night.'

The September Man stopped talking now and drew breath. He looked agitated and I felt sorry for him.

The golden-haired girl who I had started to fall in love with earlier stood up from her bench and walked towards us. She passed close to us both and gave a sidelong glance and a furtive smile – one of those smiles that drives a man mad. Then she walked away from us.

I took a few paces to follow her, but the September Man caught hold of my sleeve and I turned around and faced back towards him. I stared into the river below me for a while and when I finally turned back around the girl had vanished from my sight. I had no leads – not her name, not her phone number, no mutual friends; I didn't even know where she worked. Despite all this I felt calm.

I turned and looked towards my accomplice and he whispered in my ear, 'I have done you a favour there, mate.'

Since that day the September Man watches my every move. He is here in the Town Hall Tavern now. He is always beside me.

MEAN, MOODY AND MAGNIFICENT

People like to be in gangs. Solidarity and fraternity give most people strength and confidence and help them to speak out and express themselves more openly. People also like to be in gangs to cover up their cowardice and hide the fact that they don't have the moral strength to behave with manners and principles. I was never in a gang. I got strength from myself and I confronted my cowardice alone. It takes nothing to join the crowd, but it takes a lot to stand alone. I'm not like everybody else.

I clearly remember the Decca audition and I think I drummed particularly well that day. I always just wanted to be the drummer in a band, ever since I was a kid. Standing at the front and being the centre of attention just wasn't my thing. It was New Year's Day 1962 and it was freezing cold. We had driven down the night before and it was the first time that any of us had properly seen London Town. We walked down Charing Cross Road and we spent some time milling around Trafalgar Square and seeing a load of New Year's Eve drunks falling into the fountains. In the studio I remember thinking that the other lads got particularly nervous. Paul didn't sing as well as he could that day and John and George weren't their usual cheeky and cocksure selves. I just treated it as another session really, just drummed in my normal way. We played a lot of covers - that was Brian's idea - and none of the originals we had been doing up North. That was definitely a mistake, but I don't think that the guys that listened to those sessions understood us anyway; they came at the whole thing with the wrong mindset. I thought we played great, apart from some of the lads' nerves, but it turns out a few months later that they turned us down. Some high-up guy at the record company called Dick Rowe broke the news to Brian:

'Guitar groups are on the way out.'

An interesting opinion, but he wasn't the only one. Lots of people down South didn't see our potential. We were also rejected by Pye, Columbia, HMV and EMI. There were some other companies that said no to us too.

It was in these times of rejection that you needed to be in a gang otherwise you had indoor fireworks. You got solidarity from your gang members if you were starting to feel low and thinking that a career in music, a career that most of your family and school friends thought was just a whim, was actually going to lead you nowhere and into a life of poverty and frustration. My point here is that I was the last person to find out that we had been turned down by Decca. The others heard long before me and just let it slip out one day. Apparently they had known for weeks. Why didn't they tell me? It should have been obvious to me then that I wasn't in the gang. I didn't see it at the time.

Most of the time the gang spirit was strong and I was

conned into believing I was part of it, even if it didn't come naturally to me. I remember we used to stand at Manchester Piccadilly station or Lime Street station and John would get us into a huddle in the gloom after another slice of rejection.

'Where are we going, fellas?' he would start off.

'To the top, Johnny.'

'What top?'

'To the toppermost of the poppermost, Johnny.'

One of the other highlights for me around that time was the *Mersey Beat* popularity poll. I remember my mum showing it to me first. It was a great front-pager. We came out on top and ahead of Gerry and the Pacemakers, who were our big rival in the north-west at the time. All of the groups voted for themselves, I guess, so that any cheating would have cancelled itself out. Our prize for winning that was a headlining concert at Barnston Women's Institute. Oh, the fame and fortune.

Of course we kept going back to Hamburg and by our third trip we were playing at the Star Club, which was one of the biggest places over there. I just got my head down and got on with it. I hit the drums harder than a lot of my contemporaries and I made sure the boys had a rock solid beat for them to improvise around and do all their ad-libbing and tomfoolery. I actually enjoyed all of that stuff, even if I didn't laugh or smile as much as the other guys wanted me to.

'Why are you looking so glum, mate?'

'I am fine.'

It's just my normal blank facial expression I guess. Some people look naturally happy, some people look naturally nervous, maybe others look naturally bitchy. The girls used to say about me that I was mean, moody and magnificent. I don't think some of the other guys liked this. There were rumours that Paul and George in particular were jealous of my looks and my popularity with some of the female fans in Liverpool. Perhaps it wasn't good for the fan spirit. Perhaps they needed a less good-looking drummer. I was only the drummer, right? And that guy has to sit at the back. No lead singers want their fans looking through them or looking over their shoulder to the drummer at the back. He isn't important, he shouldn't be the person that the fans come to see.

'You are only as good as your drummer.'

Try listening to any of those songs without drums in them and see what you think…

Anyway, the Hamburg days were fun to a certain extent, but there was a massive sense of loss when Stu passed away. John obviously felt it the most, but I think that after him I was the most affected by what happened with Stu. Perhaps that wasn't very clear at the time, as I wasn't very good at showing my emotions – I tended to bury those things. We were all so young, none of us knew how to deal with death. John loved Stu, loved him more than just as a best friend. I really liked the guy, particularly because like me he wasn't really part of the gang. Stu was a painter and not really a musician. He just looked great and was a cool guy. His lack of musical ability was pissing off Paul and George and causing friction with John, who just wanted him in the band because he was his best friend. None of this stuff bothered me. I liked having Stu in the band because he was a good guy and I felt like less of an outsider when he was around. We got on well and I treasure any memories with that guy.

Brian went into overdrive after that third Hamburg visit and he managed, through all of his connections, to land us an audition with George Martin at EMI.

'Congratulations, boys. EMI request recording session. Please rehearse new material.'

So there it was. We came back from Hamburg at the beginning of June 1962. On 6th June, I think it was, we did our audition at the Abbey Road studios in St John's Wood. This time we all decided we were going to do a lot of original numbers and not just covers.

I thought it went well and then we all travelled back to Liverpool. We did a welcome home night at the Cavern and then a radio show in Manchester and then we got our heads down and focused on the northern circuit. This was the stuff I had got into playing the drums for. Relentless gigging, I loved it. This was work, this was serious and this was a groove you got into and devoured.

More music. More music. More music.

After the Cavern came the Casbah, the Majestic Ballroom, Birkenhead, the New Brighton Tower, the Northwich Memorial Ballroom, the Plaza Ballroom, St. Helens, the Hulme Hall Golf Club. The northern circuit gigs were packed out and I think that those weeks were some of the happiest of my life. We hadn't heard back from Parlophone (or I didn't think we had) and so we were just focused on high-energy white-knuckle gigging. Neil was driving us around all the time and having an affair with my mum, which was a bit odd, but didn't really affect me much at the time. We just ploughed on and on, powered by the beat of my relentless drumming.

So apparently, and I put heavy emphasis on the word 'apparently' (not the word that a gang member should use really), Brian eventually heard from Parlophone at the end of July. They wanted us to sign a contract with them. John, Paul and George were all really excited. Nobody told me. The plans were clearly in place by then. The wheels were rolling towards the act of my betrayal.

So this is what I remember now, years later and this is what I tell people when I get asked about the situation over and over again. It's funny how certain poignant events in your life appear in crystal-clear images in your memory years after the event. We were playing at the Cavern on the 15th August. It was a Wednesday evening and the weather was warm. The Cavern was hot and sweaty that night and dripping with the peak of Mersey beat rock and roll. The gig was a great one and we were due to be playing in Chester the next evening and I was supposed to be driving with John there. As we were leaving the Cavern that night I asked John what time he wanted me to pick him up for the next day's gig.

'Oh no, don't worry, mate. I will go on my own.'

This was strange as he never went to gigs on his own. He was the leader of the gang.

'How come? What's up?' I asked him, feeling a bit puzzled.

He just walked off. His face looked scared.

That night Brian rang, asking to see me and Neil at his office the next morning. So we drove down the next day and Brian looked very shaky and nervous. He was not his usual self. He was very fidgety.

'I've got some bad news for you. The boys want you out.'

The. Boys. Want. You. Out.

I couldn't speak for a while. I was in shock. I started asking why. Why were they doing this? His answers were murky and inconclusive.

'The guy at Parlophone isn't sure about your drumming.'

Really? Just one guy's opinion meant this? Were they really that hell-bent on stardom that they would sell me down the river in this situation?

'The boys aren't sure that you fit in.'

Fit in? Fit into what? What was I supposed to fit into? I played the gigs. I was a strong and consistent drummer. I was popular with the fans. What more did they want? Was I too popular with the fans? Did I pose a threat to some of them? Was it that mean and moody look that was just my natural unaffected facial expression when I wasn't talking? I couldn't do anything to prevent that. How could I?

I went and spoke to Neil outside. I had been booted out after two years and just when it looked like things were really going to take off. I didn't want to kill myself then, but I did want to kill myself later on. I wandered around a bit in a daze. I slowly drank a few pints. Brian wanted me to do a few more gigs up until the end of the week. Was he taking the piss? How could I do something like that? I was being treated just like a commodity and not like a human being.

The news broke pretty soon and it was nice to hear, in hindsight, that fans in Liverpool were upset about it too. Some of them attacked the lads and fights broke out. I heard from one source that George got injured. There were signs and pickets outside the Cavern.

19

Pete Forever. Ringo Never.

Rumours were flying round all over the place. Some were saying I had slept with one of the other's girlfriends. Some said it was because I wouldn't change my hairstyle to be like the rest of them. None of them ever spoke to me again. NONE OF THEM EVER SPOKE TO ME AGAIN.

As time has gone by I have become less angry at Brian. I believe that he liked me and didn't want to do it. As time has gone by my anger with the other three has intensified, though. Neil thought it was George that was the most responsible for it, that he really gave Brian the big push to do it, because he really liked Ringo. I don't know, I will never know I guess, but I collectively blame all three of them and their gang mentality. I don't think that any of them would have had the courage to do it on their own. I just sat at home for a few weeks and sulked. Lots of fans came by to offer their sympathy. People even camped out in the garden.

Give me some truth now, years later, anybody, if you can... Anybody...

I am still searching for the answers. As they became more and more famous, I became more and more depressed. I felt suicidal at times as they dominated the decade ahead of them and conquered the planet and made millions and millions and were loved by everyone. It was impossible to avoid them and their haircuts, their beaming faces and their new drummer. Every time you picked up a newspaper. Every time you turned on the TV. There they were. Every record shop you walked past. Every time you turned on the radio. And I had to live with this forever and live through it. The betrayal, the dishonesty and the sneakiness of the act were in my head and in my face every day for the rest of my life, an inescapable constant nightmare. It was worse than serving time in jail, I reckon, because I hadn't done anything wrong, I had committed no crime.

I became someone who couldn't bear to walk down the street or be introduced to new people, because they would want to ask me questions about it or were clearly skirting around the uncomfortable elephant in the room in all conversations. I only really found comfort in family and close friends and in people that knew me really well. I turned in on myself and didn't want to become friends with new people. But I am still alive and I didn't kill myself in the end and although I am still living through it I am a survivor.

Give me some truth, John once sang. My life is truth. My existence is truth. I never joined the gang. I made it through some really tough years and I am still alive and playing the drums. I formed my own band and we got to play the Cavern and all those other venues in the north-west again. I even became a millionaire in my sixties when the anthology albums were released and contained some songs that I drummed on. This is my story. I'm not like everybody else, but I am happy to be mean, moody and magnificent, whenever you need me to be.

THE CHANGELING

'I was there in the back stage
When the first light came around
I grew up like a changeling
To win the first time around'

Ian Curtis

Oh, Manchester, so much to answer for. I love you and I hate you, but I cannot leave you. The debauched nights spent dancing on the tables in Mojos and Sandinista. The endless bottomless nights with friends and colleagues, friends and enemies, colleagues and enemies. I have been here over ten years now and seen the sprouting of the post-Madchester world. Addicted to the mythologies of its past, Clint Boon at South Night Club, the city-centre pubs with picture after picture of Georgie Best, Eric Cantona, Tony Wilson, Ian Curtis, Morrissey.

I walk around Manchester as the autumn leaves fall and soak up the memories of ex-girlfriends, break ups, glory days and painful days. I cannot ever leave you. I want to hang around in your soundtrack. I know I have fallen deep into your man traps as I live in the past tense forever.

Up here everyone is proud to be working class. Up here people really believe in socialism and they judge you for who you are and how you treat people, rather than where you are from or how much money you have. Karl Marx lived here. The Industrial Revolution started here. The People's Movement, the Labour Movement, the Peterloo Massacre, the Sex Pistols at the Lesser Free Trade Hall. The Suffragettes came from here. Alan Turing lived here, invented the computer, cracked codes that defeated the Germans in the Second World War and was then persecuted for his homosexuality. Did he die from eating a poisoned apple? Was this the inspiration behind Steve Jobs's logo? It all came from here in one way or another. Born from some mother's womb came a nightmare situation. A blonde Hitler youth beating a drum. Manchester, I can never leave you.

This is more than the story of a city. This is a story about a rise and a fall (and a rise again?).

I had the city-centre taped. It was like my playground. Walk into the Northern Quarter and see all the aspiring bands and hang with the beatniks and the Manchester greens. In Night and Day Café, in Dry Bar and in Soup Kitchen there is so much rebel music going on. There are now more and more DIY-ethic art jobs filling the underworlds with life. I had a career flourish, I had a critical appraisal. I tasted fame after getting married young. I had to deal with all the trappings of that fame so young. All the temptations that my parents never had, that would draw me away from the provincial childhood life I once had. My imaginary friends and imaginary worlds have gone now. They are replaced forever by the excitement of the Manchester underworld.

Sometimes I venture over to Oxford Road – the Thirsty Scholar, Joshua Brooks and that real magnificent bastard the Garratt. I feel it closing in, I feel it closing in.

Sometimes back to Deansgate, back to Mojos to study the rock and roll tube map or to the Venue to measure your height on the walls against all the rock and roll legends – I was Joey Ramone or was I Elvis Presley? Don't ever fade away; I need you here with me. Let's live together in the night time.

Manchester was booming and peaking that summer. I was booming and peaking that summer too. I was riding a wave and then it happened. Then I hit self-destruct. And in fifteen hours of revelry I ruined everything. How much was I led astray? How much did I lead myself astray? Statistically it was going to happen one day. Now I feel like a changeling. Prison walls to stare at. Eight years to get through. I don't know if I can get through this. Strangeways, here we come as this cloud hangs over me. I need it. I need it so much. Manchester, I can never leave you.

I am staring at the walls. I am dreaming about the most beautiful girl in the world on the other side of the planet. Am I a changeling now? Or am I Tam Lin? A fairy child left in place of a human child and stolen by the fairies. Folklorists say it happens because of a concern over infants thought to be afflicted with unexplained diseases, disorders or developmental disabilities.

Eight years inside is hard. It changes a man forever. No sex attacks. No physical bullying. But I am a vegetarian now. I am teetotal now. I have read and read and read. Maybe this is the best thing that has ever happened to

24

me. I feel the rising surge of glorious activism spreading from my vital organs to my fingertips. Wait until I get out. I am going to change the world forever. I am going to make truly great things happen when I get out. I know now that time is finite and that every second must be cherished and not wasted. I want to change the world forever. This is the greatest thing that has ever happened to me. I want to see the Manchester streets again. Buy vinyl in Piccadilly Records on Oldham Street, walk the waterways of Castlefield, go into the Real Magnificent Bastard. Manchester, I will never leave you. I promise you that. I can see the black and yellow stripes everywhere. Don't walk away in silence. I need to rebuild my life. I am confused and I have self-hate. I don't find life as easy as you do. You make everything work so effortlessly; it will never be like that for me.

One day to go before my release and the future is unwritten. This will not be like the 18th May 1980. As long as there is a lower class, I am in it. As long as there is a criminal element, I am of it. As long as there is a soul in prison, I am not free. Manchester, you are in my blood; I can never leave you.

PRETEND YOU ARE IN A WAR

How do you prepare for the intensity of unforeseen events that crash into your life? How do you deal with them and channel the emotions into something positive? I guess just pretend you are in a war...

I wanted a revolution. This is what led me here. I wanted to break out, rebel and tear things up, but I never did because I was chained by fear. Until we met.

It wasn't a chance meeting. It was planned. I had been sent to kill him. He was outspoken and subversive. He represented something that my brothers feared – the icy truth. He talked of love and a world far removed from these troubled times. Instead of killing him, I listened and this turned out to be the most rebellious thing I have done in my life so far.

I was drawn in by his charisma and soon began to realise that my brothers' revolution was phony. They wanted a freedom for the body that would lead to more oppression, when what they needed was a freedom for the soul. It pains me to say this, but sometimes muscle isn't the answer. He made me realise this. So when he said to me earlier on tonight, 'be quick about what you are doing' it is to my soul that I travel for answers. I am interested in it right now – I am on the threshold of my deepest moment and I want to share it with you.

I remember seeing all his followers come together and watched how their early doubts were gradually erased. But I always felt distanced from them, even from the early days when I spied with stealth and purpose to the times when I was one of them. They seemed like group creatures to me, unable to stand apart from the crowd. Not me. I have stayed up talking with him around the fire when the others have fallen asleep one by one. I am closer to him than the others because of our late night dialogues. We stayed up just to talk, because we connected in a way that was unique. There were a bucketful of thoughts and revelations in the darkness. He knows this and he calls me the strongest. He will not abandon me, he will not abandon me, he will not abandon me...

The others were just eggshell men, not questioning anything until he came along. Yet I was a well-defined zealot and so my recent change has come at a price. I have endeavoured and strained, when they have only teamed up and fraternised. There is no internal conflict in Peter; he just does his thing, steady, stubborn and solid as a rock. Believe me, in another life, he has the perfect personality to be a Roman senator. 'Why is this the case, Peter?' – ROME. 'Who do your loyalties lie with Peter?' – ROME! He can be bigoted, he can be narrow-minded, but with him there is a consistency that has failed me.

I talked to my bosses recently and told them I am working for them no more. They called me a traitor, but they have not seen what I have seen and they have not heard what I have heard. I have seen dead men brought back to life by him, water turned into wine by him, the sick cured and the weak protected. He lived with and forgave a renowned prostitute. Anyone can be redeemed with him.

He is no softie though, this man. Of course I was unsure of how to feel when he healed a Roman officer's servant or when his speeches were heckled down. Some of the things he said sounded good for another world – not this one though. I had to pretend I was in a war. All the time, that was how I had to train my malleable mind. At first I didn't want to turn the other cheek. I am not a coward, I thought to myself. I don't want to love people who oppress me and when I looked at all the empty stomachs around me I wondered how love could be the answer. But then I saw his blazing temper and that inspired me so much.

He went to the temple and he tore the place up. He screamed and shouted at the high priests; he knocked over tables and stalls and threw venom at his doubters. I was in rapture for days after this.

'Roman coins have images of false gods on them and so must be exchanged for sheckles,' the self-important money-makers declared.

'I am the new law,' he retaliated and it sent shivers up my spine.

From then on there has not been any doubt in me. The seed is the word of God and my seed has fallen in good soil – I guess it is because I have a good and obedient heart.

I am ready, I am ready. There are no grey areas in my soul. If I love somebody I would die for them. If I hate somebody I would kill them. I am ready to be at one with him. I am ready to aspire to his level. His level of goodness, his level of prayer, his level of thought, who knows, perhaps his level of power. But unlike him I won't need forty days of testing to become ballsier, angrier and edgier. I have had my trials and tribulations… I am definitely ready.

He is the one and he is alone in the garden praying. Like me he is a loner. I'm not like everybody else. We are people who need to distance ourselves from the others to clarify our thoughts. I feel that strong urge for isolation too. I would be essentially the same man at any time in history and in any place. I am not someone who would compromise himself to his surroundings. I will go and talk with him once I have negotiated my way from this treacherous spot and the thirty pieces of silver in my mind. I need to eradicate that thought now. There are no thirty pieces of silver.

He has said some things recently that I wish to discuss. He has said I must give up everything I have and I will. He has said that 'he who is least among you all is the greatest' and I know this is me because I am distinct from the others in so many ways and so I am amongst them the least. But he also said 'the son of man is to be handed over to the power of human beings' and I am not sure what this means. I want to toss this one over with him for a while whilst the others are asleep. I am going to make my way there now, for he said earlier that I must be quick. But first I have to leave this place before the serpent speaks to me again.

I just have to just keep pretending I am in a war.

A ROGUE'S GALLERY

People think of pirates as outsiders and outcasts. They must have been people that did bad things and lived outside the law, to be honest. I bought a compilation album about them one time in the Northern Quarter, in one of those great record shops that you could easily spend the rest of your life in. There is a rogue's gallery on the sea, and tales and ballads interspersed with sea shanties and bullies and the good folk of Liverpool, Boston and San Francisco. The old man of the sea bathing the lovely mermaids, the Cape Cod girls, the Baltimore whores, Sally Brown, Dan Dan and the Turkish Revelry. There is an ancient world of piracy and excitement and adventure that I like to dip into. I write about it endlessly. I listened to songs about it and of course I directed my greatest award-winning movie about this topic. It is what the wider public think of when they hear my name mentioned in conversation. Let me tell you about the pirate ship this time...

I sat on the Tor last night and I remembered the stories that my father told me as a boy. This could have been Camelot, he told me. This could have been the gateway to the underworld. The sacred isle of Avalon lurked in the mist last night and I watched the twilight linger for a while, then disappear. Forgotten worlds and stories of the dispossessed came to me and I sat cold for a while in fascination. Some call it the gloaming, that half-light that is a grey area between dead and alive, and I am lucky enough to have seen it more than once: the betwixt and the between.

Dad always used to tell me about the King Arthur myth. My favourite character was Merlin – he was cool. He was dedicated to his craft and older than the hills. I was awestruck by him and I revelled in his great powers of prophecy. He could foresee the future and Arthur was nothing without him. In fact, if I recall correctly, he would never have had the chance to become king without Merlin setting up the sword in the stone situation. Merlin was pivotal to everything in King Arthur's world.

Of course, Arthur married Guinevere, 'The White Phantom', completely against the prophetic warning of Merlin. That was the bit of the story that my dad really delighted in, the courtly love between Lancelot and Guinevere. Whereas I was a Merlin man, Lancelot was my dad's guy. Whereas I felt that he and Guinevere were unfaithful to their king and deserved punishment, my dad, the old rogue, found their affair romantic and exciting. He also liked glamour and the idea of being 'the best', so he always tended to go for the swashbuckling heroes. I am drawn to the quiet ones, the thinkers, the behind-the-scenes strategists and under-rated guys. He owned biographies of Churchill, Brando, Botham and James Hunt. I read books about Gladstone, Chaplin, Brearley and Niki Lauda. These were the characters and the books that made me want to become the celebrated film director that I am today. Yet it was also this struggle with my dad and the tensions we had that shaped every major decision I made in life and every film I directed in some way or other.

Inspired by the twilight effect of sitting on the Tor, I packed the car up this morning and headed for the South coast. It had been a blisteringly hot July Saturday. The drive was smooth over the heated tarmac and my shirt became drenched with sweat all down my back. I went and sat on a breakwater by a quiet beach where my family used to play rounders when I was a boy. I like being on my own. The writer must be universal in sympathy, but an outcast by nature. I am sitting here now and I can visibly see it getting darker and the memories are coming back to me unhindered and unblemished.

My dad used to have a special whistle he would use to grab my attention in important situations. I used this as a theme for a character in my biggest film. Whether it was to help me locate him in a big crowd, or to tell me it was time to come out of the water, he'd use it and he'd use it just once and it was one of the most effective weapons in his armoury. I can hear this whistle now and it is telling me to get out of the sea because there is a storm coming. The waves are getting bigger and night is closing in. 'I'm coming,' my mind replies, which means 'give me a few more minutes' because I am warm in the rough water and my circulation is spurring me on. The waves are hitting me hard and some are taking me under. There is also a strong current, which my mother warned me about, but I want the danger. I am being taken on a journey for and against my will. What is the point of being a child if you are unable to have experiences like this?

At this point the adventure stops and the incident begins. The sea has become strangely calm and out of the sea mist I can see a ship. It is old and belongs to the era of pirate ballads and sea shanties I was telling you about. I can see it travelling, but it is moving away from me and no matter how fast I try and swim, it will always be out of my reach. At first I can see nobody on the ship's deck, but as it hits rougher water and begins to rock, I become aware of the corpses. There are scores, possibly even hundreds, of dead bodies towards the rear of the ship. Why are they here? Who are they? And who killed them? There are no living people aboard the ship as far as I can see. Who is responsible for this tragedy? Is it vengeful Poseidon or some maniacal pirate festering in the lower nooks? I imagine a bearded one-eyed storyteller, very drunk and with a mad, haughty cackle. I cannot hear the ship or smell the dead bodies, but I am old enough to know that my vision is real and young enough to know that it is accurate too.

As the ship disappears onto the horizon I hit a cold spot of water and my feet become entangled in seaweed – slippery, groping stuff, which could be warning me of rocks. I look to the beach, but it is too dark to see it and for a moment I panic, but the lights of the houses along the seashore provide some relief and a direction to head in. I swim fast and I feel no sand under my feet. I swim faster in greater disarray and confusion now – front crawl with forward lunges into the air and gasping for breath into the blackness around my face. Eventually I do reach the beach, my whole body trembling, and I am able to stand with the top half of my body out of the water. I run onto the beach and head east, hurdling each breakwater before me. I had drifted a long way. The current was strong. I run and run into my father's arms. He appeared suddenly in the darkness and I felt safe again.

The thing I remember most about the incident is not the dead bodies, the magnificence of the ship or my mother's tears. It was my father. I felt safe when I had found him, but there was also a connection – a knowing look in his eyes that night. I am sure that he had seen the ship too, although he never actually mentioned it to me. On the drive home, as my mother twittered away, we remained silent witnesses, bonded by what we had seen.

My dad died last year and I need to fill the void he has left with these pirate memories. As a husband he was a player, a cheat and a 'love rat'. As a father I hero-worshipped him and in most things he was my role model.

My own marriage has recently broken up because of infidelity, not mine but hers. Being cheated on has destroyed my soul and I am sitting here now feeling dispossessed the way that King Arthur must have done when he learnt about Lancelot and Guinevere. I have never met the Lancelot in my story, although I have no doubts that he is as handsome and gallant as my Guinevere is beautiful and wayward. If I wanted to kill this man, I would be killing my father, because my father was that man a hundred times over.

Do I destroy the thing I love or do I let it destroy me?

It's too late. The second path chose me a long time ago. We are sometimes drawn to people, not because of their admirable qualities, but because we secretly yearn to have more of their 'rascal' in us. I want him back to tell him what an arsehole he was. I want him back to change his bigoted views. I want him back to talk about the pirate ship we saw this time. I want him back to put in my rogue's gallery with Sally Brown and the Cape Cod girls and the rolling sea, with the cruel ship's captain and the 'Coast of High Barbary'. I want him back.

The pirate film I wrote and directed was a massive hit around the world. All of you readers will have heard of it at least and most probably have seen it too. There is no character in it that represents my father specifically. There is no character in it that represents me.

THE PRISON WALLS ARE CLOSING IN

I am a revisionist in many ways, but I can't turn back time. If I could I would have drowned Adolf Hitler in his paddling pool as a baby. I wouldn't have thought twice about justifying that murder. If I could turn back time.

Thursday 11th August

I finished off my report for the week at Frankfurt airport and then sent it round to all the people involved and boarded my flat to Manchester. I was feeling sleepy. It had been a long week and I had covered a lot of ground – Munich, Rosenheim, Nuremberg and Berlin. The work trip had been successful though and I was looking forward to getting back to my flat and getting a good night's sleep before working from home on the Friday.

I knew I needed to meet up with Jess at some point over the next few days. Why had she blocked me on Facebook on Tuesday? What had I done to offend her? We would definitely need to go for a coffee so that everything was cool between us, seeing as we kind of worked at the same organisation. She was a sweet girl, I had thought, brunette and pretty. James Neil was an idiot for having rejected her. She was too young for me really and I had some regret that we had slept together the week before, even if the experience felt nice at the time.

I read my book on the flight back. I was trying to read more these days. Rock and roll biographies were definitely my favourite, but I knew I needed to push myself out of my comfort zone more – I needed to read more fiction, more historical books and I needed to broaden my horizons and experiences. We touched down at Manchester airport just after eleven at night and after going through security and customs I jumped into the taxi that drove me back to my city-centre flat. The night was warm and the weekend was promising. My taxi driver told me of a heatwave coming up and a Spanish plume that the papers had been getting excited about that week. We discussed José Mourinho and the United squad for the start of the season and we talked about the Olympic Games opening ceremony that had just taken place in Rio de Janeiro. There was so much to look forward to. There was so much promise in the air that night. I just needed a good night's sleep and then I could look forward to it all properly tomorrow. The teams in Germany had done well that week and I was really nailing my job at that time too.

When I got back to my flat the key which was supposed to have been left at concierge for me by my housemate wasn't there. I went directly to the flat to see if James was in. He wasn't so I went back to the concierge. I asked again about my key and by pressing further I discovered that it had been left in a different place to normal.

My initial reaction on opening my flat was that I had been burgled. Things were thrown around the flat at unusual angles. All of the bedding had been seized from both of my beds and it appeared that all of my drinking vessels had been seized too. As I looked around in shock I saw Manchester Police papers on my coffee table. There was a search warrant and a list of all the items seized. On the very top document there was a phone number and a police officer's name handwritten and to call. What had happened here? Why had my flat been raided? Had I not paid one of my recent bills? Was I massively in debt to some energy company or something? I tried calling the number on the top sheet of paper but it just went to answerphone. I sat down on my sofa and put my head in my hands. What on earth had happened here? Why had the police raided my flat?

It took me a few minutes to gather my thoughts and make myself a glass of squash. What had happened when I left for Germany at the weekend? Who was the last person to be with me in my flat? Then it started to dawn on me – Jess. She was the last person in here with me. She left on Saturday morning. Are the police after her for something?

Friday 12th August

I couldn't sleep all night. I had no bedding and I just put some towels on top of me. It got light early and I went to call the police again. This time a woman's voice answered.

'Oh, you are back now are you?'

'Yes. I have been in Germany all week, but got back late last night. I tried calling you last night.'

'We will be round with you in twenty minutes.'

I ate some cereal and put some clothes on. Within about fifteen minutes there was a knock at the door. I opened it and a male and female police officer entered my flat and then my living room. We looked at each other hard and then it happened.

'We are arresting you for the rape of Jess Harding. Anything you say can and will be used against you in a court of law. First of all please empty your pockets.'

I sat on my sofa and put my head in my hands.

'I didn't do it. It didn't happen that way,' I am told later on were the two sentences that came out of my mouth first. I can't remember saying them. I can remember just feeling numb and feeling that everything happened in slow motion. I was driven to Swinton police station. They told me not to speak about it until I was on the record. They took my DNA and fingerprints, seized my phone and threw me in a police cell for four hours. I stared at the walls and gradually felt them close in on me. I was interviewed by the police for two and a half hours that afternoon about how I might have drugged her, how my penis entered her vagina, how I knew she wasn't asleep, and how drunk we both were at various stages of the night. They teased everything out, re-asked questions, asked trick questions, paused and paused and paused for me to trip myself up. They were very good at their job, I knew that, and strangely at an early stage this awareness gave me my first glimmer of hope, but I barely acknowledged this at the time.

'Come on, mate,' the Scouse police officer said to me at one point. 'She is a good-looking girl. You must have woken up the next morning and thought you had won the lottery.'

I was driven back to my flat around four o' clock in the afternoon and released out into jungle land, aware I was on police bail for two months and under surveillance. I was being investigated for rape with an aggravating factor, namely drugging the girl before the rape. If convicted, this offence carried an eight-year prison sentence. I would be in my late forties when I was released, probably institutionalised like Brooks out of *The Shawshank Redemption*. I would be labelled a convicted rapist for the rest of my life. And it was going to all boil down to one person's word against another – something that no one would categorically be able to prove. A matter of consent in a bedroom, that doesn't have any CCTV cameras. I thought hard about eight years in prison. I thought about how a rapist gets treated by other inmates in prison; I thought about life after the prison sentence and the 'convicted rapist' tag that would stick forever. For most of that weekend that followed my arrest I felt like I wanted to kill myself.

I had a distant awareness during that first day that this was a pivotal moment in my life. That it would change everything forever. That I would be changed forever.

We are arresting you for the rape of Jess Harding.
We are arresting you for the rape of Jess Harding.
We are arresting you for the rape of Jess Harding.
We are arresting you for the rape of Jess Harding.
We are arresting you for the rape of Jess Harding.
I didn't do it. It didn't happen that way.
I didn't do it. It didn't happen that way.
I didn't do it. It didn't happen that way.
I didn't do it. It didn't happen that way.
I didn't do it. It didn't happen that way.

Friday 5th August
I had a list of twenty-five things I had to do for work that day. I had worked a sixty-hour week in total, I reckon.

I turned my computer on at 8am and bit by bit I went through the list and ticked items off. I sent emails, I typed up notes, I worked on business cases, I made Skype calls to colleagues in Bangkok, Mexico City and Boston. At 8pm I ticked off the final item on my long list and finished off the pizza I had just cooked. It felt good. A great day of work. A great week of work. A great year. So far.

I had messaged a few friends to get them to head down to my favourite pub that night, The Garratt. I had been drinking there for six years or more. I knew the manager and most of the staff. My ex-girlfriend used to work there and it had been my work pub for a while. The Garratt was everything you needed on a Friday night after a long week of work – great jukebox, cheap drinks, big beer garden.

I put some Fudge in my hair, grabbed some chewing gum and put on a leather jacket and made my way to the pub feeling great, feeling like king of the world. Job was going great and some of the stresses and pressures of July had been lifted. I fancied a proper night out. It had been a while since I'd had one.

My good friend Katie was going to be there and she would definitely have some stories to tell me. We hadn't caught up in a while. There was likely to be a big group of people I knew at the pub too. I had texted Jess earlier in the day to try and get her to persuade as many work people to come out as possible. Jess called me in the afternoon to find out what time I was getting there and again on my walk to the pub to tell me to hurry up.

I arrived and had a drink in the beer garden and very soon Jess latched on to me. I liked Jess; she was fun. She had slept with a couple of my mates earlier in the year and this was often a topic of conversation. From some comments she had made to me I sensed that she had a bad relationship with her dad and there was something fragile there. She was definitely looking for someone to love her.

'I want you to take my Canal Street virginity tonight,' Jess said to me earlier in the evening. And so the night gathered pace and the three of us played pool and drank some cocktails. Katie didn't really know Jess from before and I was worried at an early stage that this night could be strange if they didn't get on, but they seemed to enjoy each other's company more as the evening progressed.

Rock and roll music was playing and the Madchester spirit was alive and well in The Garratt that night. As darkness fell, the streets were partially lit by the summer's full moon.

'Here you go, mate, take two of these,' the lanky stranger said to me as I walked out of the toilets around half ten and he thrust the tissues into my hands.

I walked the seven steps to the pool table and said something like, 'Some guy has just given me these.' That is all I remember. Who was that guy? I never saw him again. Was he a ghost? Was he the devil? He looked friendly and helpful, like he wanted to help me. Did anyone else know of his existence and was the moment real? In the weeks after the event I naturally scoured all the CCTV footage that I could and this strange man didn't seem to appear at any stage.

Saturday 6th August
The three of us left our other friends and headed to Canal Street around half midnight. Where did the devil go at this point? I wish I knew. I think he hung around and watched

over us all night. At times he tried to enter Jess's body and at times he tried to enter mine.

After drinking and dancing in a few bars Jess grabbed my arm and led me to the nightclub. I assumed Katie was following us, but it turns out that Jess had taken Katie's bag, phone and wallet with her so that Katie was disorientated and went home. Jess didn't tell me this until after we'd had sex the next morning.

I blacked out in the nightclub; I remember nothing for three hours. Had my drink been spiked? I hadn't had that much to drink. We burst back into the daylight at half five in the morning and I lay down horizontally in the car park and Jess filmed me on my phone and we goofed around for a while. Why did she film me on my phone? She had a smartphone of her own.

Then the taxi back to mine.

Then the glasses of water.

Then the kissing.

Then the kissing in bed.

Then the kissing on the neck.

Then the sleeping for me.

Then the sleeping for her? Or the lines of cocaine? Or the plotting? Or the drugs plant?

Then the waking up in a spooning position.

Then the massaging the back.

Then the foreplay.

Then the moaning.

Then the kissing.

Are you ok?

Yeah.

Then taking each other's clothes off.

Then the tentative and slow sex with passionate kissing.

Then the momentum gradually building.

Then her grabbing my back.

Then the faster sex with bodies in synchronization.

Then the urge to change positions.

Whoa, I think we should just chill out for a minute.

We talk for a while. We discuss her movements that weekend and we piece the night together and she reveals that she has all Katie's things. We also discuss whether anything is going to be awkward between us in the future. I don't think it will be. She isn't so sure.

Then the devil appears again as I notice a bag of white powder on my coffee table. It wasn't there last night. I casually mention it to her and she looks sheepish and guilty and doesn't say anything and doesn't take it. It is definitely hers, not mine. And it wasn't there when we started kissing and went into the bedroom. She gets a taxi, but she has left her druggy bank card on my bedroom floor. We exchange some friendly texts about this. I say that I will leave it for her at concierge. She says thanks, she does need it, but that it can wait until Monday. I tell her thanks for looking after me, she deserves a medal. I go for lunch and return Katie's stuff. I sleep in the afternoon. Jess messages me that evening: 'Don't tell anyone about last night. Not Dave. Not Simon. No one.'

'Sure, fine, don't worry about it,' I respond.

Sunday 7th August

I fly to Germany. I like Jess, but I feel regret about the age difference and the work connection. I switch my mind into work mode and I arrive at my hotel late in the evening.

Monday 8th August

I text Jess at lunchtime, telling her all about my day and the crazy things that are going on in Germany. Maybe I will take her to a musical next week? I get no response and feel a bit miffed.

Then the next day she blocks me on Facebook.

Then I start to stress a little.

Then I try calling her.

Then my flat gets raided by the police.

Then I fly home.

Then it all kicks off and I get arrested and questioned and bailed and humiliated.

Then a work colleague runs away from me when she sees me on the street.

Then I break down in tears.

Then I spend hours online learning about rape convictions and what life is like in Strangeways. What you are allowed and not allowed in prison, how you get treated in your first few weeks, how other prisoners treat convicted rapists.

Then I want to kill myself.

Then the police try and re-arrest me for breach of my bail. I was reported by Simon at work for being seen near the office. I thought this guy was my friend. What a traitor.

Then I learn all about her rape allegations in the past.

Then I learn a million things about Jess I never knew from her friends.

Then I know that the devil was dancing alongside both of us all night.

Then I have the sleepless nights.

Then I have the recurring nightmares.

Then I have the people rejecting me and turning their back on me.

Then there are the people with no backbone.

Then there are the people with backbone.

Then there is my support network of people that I really love.

Then there is the music I really love.

Then there is her playing tricks and trying to get me to break my bail.

Then I hear she said she wants me to get eight years.

Then I hear she said to someone that she knows that I have raped other girls before.

Then I hear she has got a big payout.

Then I fade in and out and in and out of moods and I sit and sweat it out with the devil on my shoulder.

Waiting and waiting.

Will the police do their job well?

I am the only person who knows I am innocent. Jess knows it, but it is buried deep in her. Why the false allegation? Attention, sympathy, vengeance, money, psychopathic delusion? A combination of all of these?

Waiting and waiting.

Four months in and I am still on bail, I am still under investigation and I am still suspended from work and unable to talk to anyone from work. Everything about my future is hanging in the balance.

The prison walls are closing in.

WHISTLE DOWN THE WIND

'If you just love all the people that love you where does that get you? Even the biggest scum on earth love the people that love them.'

I remember when she came up to me at first. She came up to me to kiss me and my initial feeling was one of excitement. Those great lips and the tense eye contact. Then I realised that it was being done to betray me and I tried my best not to hide the fear that was building up inside me. The crowds surrounded me. The people looked hostile – they had guns and sharp knives. There were even children looking at me angrily as if I was a murderer or a rapist or a paedophile.

Ok, so I got arrested; what was I supposed to do then? I tried to just stay calm and not let my inner emotions show. I wanted to cry, but I didn't cry. I wanted to say a million things that were in my head about the world and injustice and poverty and corruption, but my motor skills failed me. I guess to the people around me I looked poised and on top of my emotions, but I promise you I wasn't. Whilst this was how I was feeling, the people around me lost their heads and started behaving irrationally.

As I was put in the van and driven away, a mate of mine was being asked questions by someone in the hostile crowd.

'You know that guy, right? He is a mate of yours, isn't he?'

'No, I don't know him.'

'Come on. I have seen you hanging round with him. You are thick as thieves you two.'

'Look, I told you, I don't know the guy.'

'You look as guilty as sin mate. I bet you and him were into loads of dodgy stuff together. Guilty by association.'

My mate just walked away and didn't respond the way he should have done. He didn't defend me. He didn't have my back at all. I guess that most people behave selfishly when there is a state of panic and turmoil around them. That street scene haunted me throughout the rest of my suffering.

I got held hostage by some barbaric people and they took great pleasure in mocking me because I was weak and vulnerable. I felt like a circus animal being taunted and mocked and beaten by the people that were guarding me. I got blindfolded as I was being hit.

'Who hit you?'

'Have a guess,' said the other one. 'Me or him?'

'Pathetic.'

And they kept on taunting and having fun with me throughout the evening. I was crying and screaming now. This was the price I was having to pay.

I knew at this point that I was going to die a slow and painful death. I wasn't aware of anyone that could genuinely stop this from happening. Well, actually there was one guy. High up in the law department and powerful and intelligent. People went to him to tell them all my made-up hideous crimes.

'He has done this to other people.'

'He is obsessed with sadism.'

'He has always been a twisted and perverted human being.'

'Evidence? I need hard evidence,' the law man said and I hear it silenced the baying group.

He could have done more to help me at this point, I suppose, but he was probably a busy guy with other pressing engagements. He could have saved my life, but he sat on the fence. He washed his hands of the situation and moved his brain on to the things that were more important in his life. He probably didn't think about me that much after this had happened. Everyone has a priority list in their head about who they need to devote their attention to in life and the issues that matter most to them. Why go out on a limb to be principled? Why put yourself at risk or danger for someone else? It is so much easier to follow the crowd and it is so much easier to be practical. The law man didn't want to risk his position and reputation for me. He had ambitions and plans of his own that needed to be fulfilled.

I then spent some time in confinement, alone with my thoughts. I lost track of minutes and hours and days. I lost track of day and night. Sometimes short periods of time felt like an eternity, sometimes longer periods of time passed quickly. I was alone and weeping, but I knew that this pain would end and that was the only thing that gave me comfort.

Eventually they came for me and took me out into a public place to end my life. They dragged me away and ridiculed me. It wasn't these people's fault though; they were just acting under orders, just doing what they had been told. You have to forgive them, because getting angry solves nothing. If you love the people who hate you and teach others to do the same it is the only way to make things better.

They took me to a place called The Skull and that is where they killed me.

'Look at him now. All his grand words have come to nothing.'

'I feel sick just looking at him.'

'He is getting what he deserved.'

Parents told their children that this was what happened when you became too greedy or tried to break rules. I was being held up as an example of a person to ridicule and hate.

I think I died slowly. Fading in and out of consciousness and believing I was dead and then coming back to life again. The cacophony of noise around me as the stones hit me became more and more distant.

I remember staring at a young girl wearing a brown dress. She must have been around ten years old and she was motionless and silent. Her features were in focus in my mind and it seemed that she was the only person in the crowd that was not rejoicing at my pain and suffering. I saw a hint of concern in her naïve face and that was the last thing I think I saw as the blood drained from me and the spasms clinched my entire body. There was human spirit and strength in isolation in that crowd and the girl in the brown dress embodied all of my passion and love. All the things I had cared about in the world – the people and the music and the places – all these things and more

50

were a part of her aura as I gently faded in and out of consciousness and slipped away from the world.

I came to set the earth on fire.

I came to whistle down the wind.

I did terrible, terrible things in my life and I deserved what happened to me. But the girl in the brown dress knew that I died a happy man, knowing that you have to love the people that hate you. I died knowing that someone cared.

HOPE NOT HATE

They were planning to build a new mosque in Oldham and it was causing a stir. All manner of far right groups were planning on joining the demonstration that Saturday afternoon. People of all different religions and political opinions and many with none of each were looking at the centre of town that day to see what was going to happen. It was a drab October Saturday. There wasn't much in the way of entertainment. The local football team were playing on the Sunday instead so the hardcore fans had nothing better to do. Sunil left his parents' house around one o'clock and met up with a few university friends before heading into the centre of town. He knew that it was going to kick off.

Sunil was from a Muslim family. He had grown up in Oldham, but gone away to university in Sheffield. Although his parents were fairly devout, Sunil had a well balanced approach to British life. He was proud to be a British Muslim. He prayed and fasted and knew the most important passages of the Koran, but he also enjoyed a pint of bitter and had friends at university from all ethnic backgrounds. At university you could escape the divisions that small-minded people wanted to impose on British society. Sunil and his mates all looked out for each other and wanted to get on in life and be successful in their various vocations and potential careers. Back in Oldham for the weekend though and Sunil was instantly reminded of all the hate groups on both sides of the Islam debate and everything that he had wanted to escape from. These people spoke endlessly about the murder of Lee Rigby, about Sharia law and Anjem Choudary. The reasons for 9/11, the Israel/Palestine debate – one man's terrorist was another man's freedom fighter. The Rochdale grooming gangs, the lynchings of the National Front, the holocaust-denying Nick Griffin of the BNP... hideous acts on both sides, horrible arguments and indefensible people. Sunil had left Oldham to get away from all this. He wanted hope not hate, but somehow through a morbid curiosity he found himself walking into the centre of town just as the anti-mosque demonstration was getting into full swing.

Johnny had lived in Oldham all his life and was heading down to the demonstration at the same time as Sunil. He was well known in town as the previous leader of a far right group that opposed what he called the Islamisation of Britain. But he had left the organisation after spending some time in prison for mortgage fraud and was now trying to work with more peaceful organisations to bring about change.

No one had seen Johnny in the town centre since he had come out of prison. He had Muslim enemies because of his far right past. He had new Muslim friends since becoming more of a moderate. He also had a Muslim ex-girlfriend in Oldham, who was now married with children. Some say that she was the love of his life and her family's racist and aggressive attitude towards him as a teenager was the catalyst that drove him to become the activist and political leader that he became famous for. Originally he joined the BNP when he was still doing his GCSEs, but he left them when he learnt that non-whites couldn't join the party. That wasn't for him, that wasn't his vision.

Johnny was a married man with two children. His wife ran a sunbed business in town. He was a big Oldham Athletic supporter and had run their fan club at one point too. He walked into town wearily and on his own that Saturday lunchtime. He looked like a man who had suffered a lot over the years. He looked like someone who wanted peace now. His thuggish haircut and head shape belied a gentle disposition and a warm smile that endeared him to many. The biggest worry for Johnny that afternoon was whether he would run into some of the neo-Nazis and fascists that he had tried to get expelled and kept out of his party for years. They saw him as a traitor for sympathising with British Muslims now. Some of them could get violent at the drop of a hat and so Johnny was always looking around him and making sure that he was in a safe crowd and not likely to get cornered at any point. Johnny was no angel – you could still sense that his temper could boil over if he was provoked enough and he still sometimes wore a bulletproof vest in public. Yet Johnny was a bruised and battered soul. Johnny wanted hope not hate now.

Jessica was already in the town centre and campaigning – this was her big day. She was the deputy leader of Taking Our Country Back. At thirty years old she was the darling of the party. Dark-skinned, with a curvaceous body and wearing lots of make-up, she was the poster girl of the far right. Most of the men in the party wanted to sleep with her, but were also intimidated by her brash and ballsy 'man-eater' approach. Jessica wanted hate disguised as hope.

Jessica had organised this demonstration and had galvanised all her fans and supporters to be there. She was handing out leaflets and whipping up controversy and hatred with her every move. Her new boyfriend Dean, a twenty-four-year-old skinny but good-looking skinhead, had come to the demonstration too. He wasn't very politically minded but he knew that he had to impress Jessica today, particularly as she was surrounded by loads of hot-blooded sycophants who drooled over her every move.

Sunil and Johnny (who didn't know each other) stood side by side and watched Jessica in action. Sunil felt so angry at the way this woman was talking to Muslim women, provoking them with insults and then having her film team record their responses in a way that made Jessica look like the victim. This made Johnny angry too, but his body language and demeanour was more world-weary and resigned – he disliked Jessica, but he had seen it all before. In many ways she resembled Johnny years before and this was something he was finding unpleasant to watch. He went and bought himself a burger and chips and just wished that Oldham Athletic were playing a Saturday afternoon fixture instead.

'The prophet Muhammad was a paedophile,' shouted Jessica as she handed out her Taking Our Country Back leaflets. Sunil and his friends were starting to feel more and more anger. This woman was twisting something they loved into a terrifying propaganda display.

'He married her when she was six. He had sex with her when she was nine,' shouted Jessica.

'The Koran says that Muslims are to cut off the heads of disbelievers.'

'Muhammad says that women are deficient in intelligence. That a witness statement of a woman is worth half that of a man.'

'Zakat funds terrorism.'

'Oldham doesn't resemble a British town any more. Let's take our country back!'

Jessica was getting loud cheers and was now using a microphone and the majority of the demonstration was centred around her. The crowd was loving her now and Jessica's boyfriend Dean was right at the front waving his arms around wildly and clenching his fists. Sunil and his other Muslim friends stood further back from the crowd looking bewildered and enraged at the hatred that this woman was inciting.

There was a heavy police presence and they were calling for backup. Things were about to turn ugly any minute and the boys in blue were panicking.

'This is a Christian country,' screamed Jessica directly at the police.

Jessica seemed to shout this sentence every thirty seconds. She had a reputation for organising Christian patrols and mosque invasions, something which caused the original party leader to resign. She had become more powerful than him and her overwhelming hatred had actually brought out some goodness in the old man.

Jessica continued raging against multiculturalism, immigration, political correctness and the Islamification of Britain. Jessica was using her hate as a weapon. It was hate disguised as hope and the crowds lapped it up.

'Muslims who die fighting non-Muslims are promised seventy-two virgins in paradise.'

'The word racism was invented by a communist mass murderer to silence European opposition to multiculturalism.'

'We will not rest until every traitor is punished for their crimes against our country. And by punished I mean good old-fashioned British justice at the end of a rope.'

As Jessica continued to whip the crowd up into a frenzy, Johnny noticed a neo-Nazi skinhead from his past approach some of Sunil's friends from behind. Without any warning this man smashed a glass bottle over one of the young Muslim men's heads. Blood poured everywhere and before anyone had a chance to respond a group of young Muslims ran in to start beating up the neo-Nazi. As soon as this had happened some more neo-Nazis ran over and started pummelling the other Muslims. Johnny ran in, even before the police did, and tried to break the fight up. He had seen enough bruises and blood and hatred in his life and he didn't want any more in the hometown that he loved today. It was far too late now though.

Jessica stood up on a bench near the battle and watched the chaos around her. The majority of her young male supporters, including her boyfriend Dean, joined in the brawl as the police started to get involved and the whole of Oldham town centre seemed to become a war zone.

At this point Jessica's boyfriend Dean attacked Sunil. He caught hold of Sunil's hair and was pulling it with the back of his hand, and then seizing him by the neck he flung him to the ground. Then Sunil, mad with rage, his temples swollen and his eyes suffused with blood, started throttling the young white skinhead with one hand, whilst punching him furiously in the face with the other. They both struggled wildly, but Sunil started to win their own private duel. He pinned Dean down and went on punching him, without drawing for breath and without really knowing where his blows were falling. Blood flowed freely while Dean, choking and gasping for breath, spat out broken teeth and struggled in vain to shake off Sunil.

'Why are you doing this to me?' Sunil kept shouting, and after he had won his fight he walked away through the crowd. 'This is not me, this is not me,' were the words running through his frenzied head.

Johnny was running from honourable duel to honourable duel, trying to break fights up as Jessica watched over the scene she had created with private delight. She didn't even notice until a long time later that her new boyfriend had taken such a beating. His well-being was not what mattered most to her. Her brain was thinking already of the headlines and the media angles and the recorded messages that she would send out on YouTube to her thousands of supporters later that week. Dean was replaceable after all; there were thousands like him.

Thirty-six men were arrested that afternoon in Oldham town centre. Johnny, Dean and Sunil were not part of that group. No one died, but many people were seriously injured and footage of the demonstration and the subsequent riot made the main news that evening and the next day. The clashes were reported as violent and drunken and households of people watched in horror at fighting scenes that showed no evidence of the baiting and provocation of Jessica and her microphone.

Johnny took a few hits but left the scene to go back to his family that evening and a quieter life that meant he would never go to jail again or make the kind of headlines he had before. He worked with the Quilliam Foundation for a while, but became disillusioned with politics and expanded his and his wife's sunbed business and went to every single Oldham Athletic home game.

Dean was not seriously injured in the brawl, but never spoke to Jessica again after that day and kept away from right-wing politics – it was never really his thing anyway.

Sunil went back to Sheffield University and continued his medicine degree, ashamed of what had happened in his hometown and traumatised by the beast that it unleashed in him.

Jessica Nilsson took the train back to Mansfield the next day. She boarded the connecting train in her green jacket with its political slogan and sat alone at a four-person table. Two young lads who had watched the news the night before, but were impartial to the issues around the building of a new mosque in Oldham, came and sat opposite her. One of them slowly recognised who she was from her many YouTube videos. She noticed fairly quickly that this young man recognised her and she winked at him. The young man blushed a little and looked away. Jessica looked out of the window and held a photogenic pose for the young lad to keep looking up at throughout the two-hour train journey. She wanted plenty more demonstrations, plenty more mosque invasions and plenty more sycophantic admirers.

LIKE A PUNK ROCKER IN 1977

I had been planning to kill someone for a while. Life was getting pretty mundane in the mid-seventies. Britain was a stagnant place and the north of England was more bleak and grey than it had ever been before. The excitement and energy of the sixties had dissipated and lads like me were about to experience all the drabness of the Callaghan era, the winter of discontent and the painful and nauseating sounds of prog rock and the Canterbury movement. Did anyone ever feel energised or radicalised by the instrumental solos of Wishbone Ash or Emerson, Lake and Palmer?

I decided that if I was going to kill someone I had to do it meticulously. The preparation and planning would be as much of the juice in this situation as the actual act itself. The question was, who was I going to kill? Who was going to be the chosen one?

I was living on my own at the time, so I could plot everything and write everything down on paper and leave these bits of paper on my desk or stuck to the walls of my bedsit. No one ever came to visit me, so there was no risk of anything leaking out to the wider world. The only person that ever came to my door was the postman. The longer I spent on my own and without an actual job, the more my ideas started to take shape. Isolation breeds creativity and madness, two of the most important ingredients for a killer. I had some music on my record player from time to time to help me punctuate my daily routines. I had a fondness for the early Manchester punk bands of that time – Slaughter and the Dogs and The Buzzcocks. Short, sharp and snappy tunes about taut and tormented emotions – the soundtrack for a killer like me.

The decision-making process had a lot to do with location and I lived in Audenshaw. I had no preference over the age, race or gender of the person I was going to kill. I didn't mind if someone was black or Asian or white and I didn't hate men more than women or vice versa. I just wanted to kill someone who deserved it and had it coming to them. So it needed to be someone nearby that I could observe for a while and grow to dislike.

Do you think I am mad?

Are you reading this now and thinking I am a psychopath?

If so you are correct on both counts. I had become aware of everything in heaven and hell. It was the events going on around me on earth that I was numb to and wanted to be disassociated from. I had no one in my life that I loved and as an only child who was estranged from his parents I had no one who loved me either. I lived in a loveless universe and needed something to give me a lasting thrill. Something that could make me infamous and define my life. The seventies really were that bad and Britain was in dire need of a shake up too. The fact that I could hear many things going on in hell at the time, did that make me mad? No, I was bound by it and it gave me the sense of destiny that warmed me at night.

I picked a man in his forties that lived half a mile away. Once I had picked him, the idea of killing him fascinated me day and night. There was nothing obvious to dislike about this man, there was nothing much to like about him either. He seemed to represent the dullness that was suffocating me at that time of my life. He read The *Times* newspaper on the way to work every day and dressed in a grey suit and tie. I never saw him smile. I never saw any emotion. I never saw any good manners. For a few weeks I watched this balding middle-aged man leave his house at eight o'clock every morning and get into his car and drive to work. He looked smug and self-satisfied with his middle-class life, yet he looked like he had no enjoyment or passion for anything. At weekends I noticed that he rarely left the house and spent most of his time watching television or mowing his lawn.

One day I followed him to the local shops and overheard him talking to a young girl behind the counter in the newsagents with a condescending and dismissive tone. He thought he was better than her and she was visibly affected by his derision. His lack of manners was so evident. He symbolised what the politicians of the seventies had created. There was no such thing as society in his head and if everyone in Britain was like him then we were approaching an apocalypse.

He was the chosen one.

He deserved to die.

Have you ever sat and listened all the way through to *The Yes Album* and decided that it made you want to be a killer? I have many times, but I needed the opposite to put my plans into action. The brooding desires came from the stultifying prog rock. The motivation to act came from punk, and its two minute jolts of energy were the litmus paper that I needed once I had identified my target.

You still think I am mad? Trust me, madmen know nothing. I am more than mad. I left that state a long time ago.

I befriended this man first of all. I did it subtly by talking to him on his way home from work a few times. I told him I lived nearby and asked him what team he supported. City? Yeah, I supported them too and we talked a little about the glory years of the last decade. His observations were flimsy and there was no real love of the game there, but I was friendly enough to build up some rapport with him. Once I had his trust I was able to get him to come round my house and within minutes I knocked him out.

Would a madman have been as wise as this?

Would a madman have been playing 'New Rose' off *Damned Damned Damned* at the time?

Once he was unconscious I laid him down in my pantry and looked at him hard. There was nothing about this man to like. I wanted to kill him so much. I shone a torch on his face for a while and studied his features. I decided to keep him alive for a while, but sedated. And then every few hours I would break boldly into the pantry and watch him. I spoke to him, calling him by name in a hearty tone and enquiring how his day went. How did he feel about the girl he had ordered cigarettes from? Did he still feel better than her? Did he still feel smug that his life was better than hers?

A few days and nights passed and he awoke on

occasions but was tied up and unable to move. He was gagged too and only occasionally did I allow food or water to pass his lips.

After three days I cautiously moved him (whilst still sedated) into my kitchen. The minute hand of a watch would have moved quicker than mine on this evening. Never before that evening had I really understood the power I now held over this man's life. I could scarcely contain my feelings of excitement!

You still think I am mad? No, you are wrong now. I had sobered up from my madness and was acting with calculated precision. Like the kind of guitar solo I had grown to hate, yet knew had technical virtuosity.

I kept my man gagged in the kitchen. I didn't let him speak. I knew that he had nothing to say that would interest me or hold any relevance to the grey world outside.

I stayed still for long periods, watching him. Seeing his eyes open and close and watching him move in and out of consciousness. He was sat bolt upright on my kitchen floor as I gained greater and greater power over him. At times I even felt like I could hear his heart beating and permeating the air around us. The hellish tattoo of his heartbeat grew quicker and quicker and I started to believe that he was more alive than me.

It was the fourth day of his captivity and he was looking pale. I had allowed him water and some soup at varying intervals, but now we were closer together on that kitchen floor and I was having brotherly feelings towards this middle-aged grey man.

Was I becoming less mad? Were the seventies nearing an end and my paranoid feelings becoming diluted? I started watching him for longer periods and I felt less anger. Maybe it was me that needed to die. Maybe this man deserved to live and I deserved to die. His pain was becoming more and more apparent to me and I was becoming more and more nervous.

Did he have a mother who loved him?

Unlike me.

Did he love someone out there in this city?

Unlike me.

Was his appearance of banal existence a smokescreen for a life of honour and integrity?

On day five I left him in the kitchen and paced around the garden. I was playing no more music by this point and the inspiration for my final act was dying within me. The garden was alive with insects and flowers and pollen. This swelled my brain. The man on my kitchen floor was asleep, but a peaceful prisoner now.

My nervousness was becoming more and more apparent. And now at the night time in the garden I was pacing around frantically.

Am I less mad now? Am I more like everybody else? How was I to kill this man now? Was the chase better than the catch? What would day six of the captivity bring?

Day six arrived and the doorbell rang. I didn't answer. There was no evidence I was in and I had no car, no neighbours that knew me, no lights on in the house. Was it the man's family? Had I underestimated his impact on the world (greater than mine)? Was it the police, coming to arrest me (again)? The doorbell rang three times and I didn't answer. My man was still gagged and bound on the kitchen floor. There was no way that anyone could know what was happening. Yet he knew, as his ears were not blocked, that there was hope and that a rescue was potentially imminent.

I waited a few hours and then went back to the kitchen. I decided that this was the last day and so I started talking to him softly.

'Are you happier now, than you were yesterday?'

His eyes were manic – filled with puzzle and terror.

'Do you think I am going to kill you? Do you think that this is what I had planned all along?'

Of course he couldn't answer any of these questions, but I kept on tormenting and stimulating his re-awakened brain.

'What are the things that matter to you in life? What do you care about the most?'

He looked at me intensely, bug-eyed with fear.

He was trying hard to answer now and for the first time I saw passion and emotion run through his pathetic body.

'If I don't kill you and I let you live, will you be a better person than you were before?'

If I don't kill you and I let you live will you be a better person than you were before? I kept repeating this sentence over and over in my head. The madness had gone now, the dullness of my life had gone. The country was going to get better. Punk rock would become new wave and there would be a freshness and a hope for all the kids out there.

I need to let this man live.

I need to let this man live.

The doorbell rang again and this time I could see it was the police and one of them saw me through the living room window.

I grew pale and I started talking to myself with a

heightened voice. I needed to let the police in. I had no intention to kill now. Should I kill myself? But no, this was never something I had planned. The thought flew through my brain, but I also realised that I wouldn't know how to do it.

The doorbell rang for the seventh and eighth time. I knew that I had to answer it soon or the police would force entry. I could no longer hear anything in heaven and I could no longer hear anything in hell.

There was now a group of people standing behind the police at the door, as if the whole of Audenshaw had found their suspect. One of them was even dressed as a punk rocker.

I gasped for breath. I continued talking to the man on my kitchen floor, louder and louder.

'If I don't kill you and I let you live, will you be a better person than you were before?'

I walked to my front door and started to unlock it, but I paused before the final movement and smiled. My job was done and my role was complete. I could feel a sense of satisfaction. I turned the key for the final time and opened the door to see the hypocritical faces of the police officers standing in front of me. I kept a calm demeanour and told them all that their search was over. The man they were looking for was safe and well in this house. He hasn't gone mad, I told everyone, and he may just be a better person than he was before.

COCO LOUISE SPARKLES

Sometimes it is the people no one imagines anything of,
who do the things that no one can imagine.

Alan Turing

I have been a transvestite every weekend for the last five years now. Monday to Friday I am a very feminine Jeff and I work in an office in the centre of Manchester. Just a skinny queer boy from the Isle of Man. However, on the weekends I am Coco Louise, platinum blonde and tarty with pigtails and stilettos. The best-looking drag queen on Canal Street. The one that turns all the heads, even the straight boys' heads. I am Coco Louise and I sparkle – boy, do I sparkle.

I started cross-dressing as a gay teenager, but I couldn't come out on the Isle of Man. It's probably the worst place for that and my parents would have really struggled to understand it all. They are both deeply religious and going to church on a Sunday was a big part of growing up for me. I was confirmed at the age of fifteen and regularly attended church and Holy Communion. I prayed all the time and I knew the Bible really well, but I knew that at any moment I needed to break away and make my butterfly transformation into a woman. I knew that Jesus

68

wouldn't disapprove and I think of him always, which is why I always carry a crucifix in my bag, but I was far less confident about my mum and dad.

I needed to go to a big city where there was a community of other people that wanted to cross-dress and that wanted to be T-girls too. Just being a gay lad was never going to be enough for me. I wanted to stand out from the crowd and I wanted to be a unique individual that straight men desired. I didn't fancy gay men, I fancied the straight ones. Ever since I had left school I had known that I wanted to get fucked by straight men and not gay men. I wanted to mess with their minds as well as their bodies – that was the appeal for me. The most potent sexual organ in the human body is the brain.

I started getting hormone replacement therapy when I was eighteen and then surgical procedures to feminise my voice, skin, Adam's apple, face, waist, breast, buttocks, genitals – the whole deal. I decided that I wanted to be like Marilyn Monroe and so I put pictures of her everywhere in my bedroom – her transformation from Norma Jean had a profound impact on me at an early stage.

I learnt and read a lot about the history of being transgender. In Japan they call us Futanari and in Germany they call us Damenwaschetrager. In Mexico, the Zapotec culture includes a third gender in the form of the Muxe. Amongst the Middle Eastern Akkadian people a Salzikrum was a person who appeared biologically female, but had distinct male traits. In Samoan culture there is a specific role for male-to-female transgender individuals, known as Fa'afafine. Many Native Americans even acknowledge the existence of a third gender – there is the Zuni male-bodied

La'mona, the Lakota male-bodied winkte and the Mohave male-bodied alyhaa and female-bodied hwamee. They say these people have two spirits. I have two spirits too, but in reality I just wanted a good time.

The gay village in Manchester became my second home and every Friday and Saturday night I got dressed up and went to all the classic haunts – the Rembrandt, Churchills, Napoleons, Kiki, Cruz 101, AXM. The only time of year I really gave the place a miss was the Manchester Pride weekend at the end of August – too many people jumping on the bandwagon that weekend in my opinion. People who once a year thought it was cool and hip to go to gay clubs and get themselves all painted up. That annoyed me so I went abroad around that time every year. Being Coco Louise is no part-time matter; it is a way of life living this way and it is important that Coco Louise sparkles.

As a community we have to deal with a lot of violence and transphobia. There have been a series of murders on Canal Street and bodies thrown into the actual canal. It's terrifying and we are all on our guard. Although the city is as tolerant and open-minded as anywhere in the Western world, there are still lone wolves out there who could strike at any moment. The drag queens, the admirers, the gender-fluid: we could all be targets at any given time.

Then there is the HIV issue. People say that one in five people in the village carry the virus and that this fraction is growing all the time. People like to go bareback in the village – they like the risk, they like the thrill. You can get PEP now, they say. It isn't a death sentence like it was for people like Freddie Mercury or Arthur Ashe or Rock Hudson. Many of my friends like to live dangerously and so they are prepared to take that risk. A couple of visits to the Hathersage Centre each year and they are calm about what they are doing.

I wanted to be like a cross between Joanna Jet and Paris Lees. The former is a London-born transvestite porn star goddess that I worshipped and had pictures of all over my bedroom wall. The latter is a transgender activist from Hucknall in Nottinghamshire and previously the deputy editor of the *Gay Times*. Paris committed robbery aged sixteen and spent eight months in jail, whilst still a boy. Then she went off to Brighton University and the butterfly transformation happened. The butterfly became gorgeous, but possessed a sharp wit and had fierce and prickly opinions that mirrored mine. I can't talk or write like Paris, but I can fuck like Joanna Jet. If I am in the mood.

I started off as a wannabe in my first year in Manchester. I watched lots of Joanna Jet porn and I stuffed socks down my bra initially. I looked into using a dressing service and befriending other 'girls' on the scene. At this stage though I had very few clothes, wigs, make up or anything else for that matter. There was some fear in me of the potential for public ridicule. Would a horde of tranny bashers hunt me down and beat me up? Would lots of people laugh at me? Then I became a beginner, with my burning desire to dress as a woman. I found most of the other 'girls' really welcoming and quickly became friends with Shaffire and Tamzin. There was the odd 'bitch', usually older and usually jealous of the better-looking younger ones. Once into my stride and into my second year on the scene I was able to pick up men and admirers every Friday and Saturday night.

I started having a lot of sex. A lot of sex whilst surrounded by loads and loads of Marilyn Monroe pictures in my bedroom.

The dichotomy of transvestite sex is that having sex usually involves removing all of your clothing, yet it is actually the wearing of those clothes that stimulates the sexual excitement in the first place. A transvestite without clothes is just a man, and is anybody going to be that interested in that?

So I am going to tell you a story about a Saturday night out that I had a while ago. I go out to pick up straight men. I am not a prostitute and never have been. I have a full-time day job so don't need the money and don't want to have to fuck guys that I don't fancy. I like to pick up the younger, slimmer, straight ones and I love all the mind games that go with the initial flirtation and pick up.

I dressed up in a St. Trinian's schoolgirl outfit and had my hair in pigtails as usual. I wore sharp high stilettos that night – they are named after a blade right? Well, their danger excited me more than ever on this particular Saturday night. Some nights I wore slingbacks, some nights T-bars; I also liked mules, espadrilles, Mary-Janes and kinky thigh-high boots. But this was definitely a stiletto Saturday. I wanted to take a straight man's cherry and do it with some style.

I drank Prosecco at my flat with Tamzin and when we were in the right sort of state we got a taxi to the village and entered Napoleon's about half one. We made an entrance alright. Two hot drunk stunners on the prowl. We were loud and brash and we expected men to buy us drinks and drool over us and they were queuing up. Problem is that it was all the usual old-school scene admirers in there to begin with. Old men with balding heads and out-of-shape physiques. I just focused on talking to Tamzin and pouting whenever I could. Then I saw this younger lad enter the bar on his own. He must have been about twenty-one, around six foot tall, and black and handsome in a wholesome and innocent way. I gave him a long lingering glance and he seemed transfixed. Yeah, this was the straight boy that I was going to fuck tonight.

I decided to approach him as I sensed that Tamzin and I were potentially too intimidating otherwise.

'Hey there sailor. You look like you are horny tonight.'

'I d-d-d-don't really know how to respond to that.'

'You are doing a pretty good job. Come on, let's go onto the dancefloor together.'

His stutter endeared me to him straight away and he warmed up as we danced closer and closer to each other. Then I grabbed him and started kissing him with as much passion as I could. I could see out of the corner of my eye that Tamzin was jealous of my instant success and she had lured an older guy onto the dancefloor opposite me and was putting the moves on him.

After twenty minutes I decided I wanted to take this young black man home and I grabbed him by the arm and took him out to the row of black cabs outside. I could tell he was really shy and nervous. He talked a little in the cab about his student life and that he was a loner. I could tell he hadn't been fucked properly before, but I could also tell that his curiosity was running away with him.

Once in the flat I put some music on and poured two large whiskey and cokes and we sat close to each other on my sofa. My phone was going off in my pocket, so I decided to turn it off. We talked some more and I poured two more large whiskey cokes. I wanted to make my move, but I decided to tease him first.

'Have you been with someone like me before?'

'N-n-n-no, this is my first time.'

'Don't worry. I will be gentle. I will break you in slowly.'

I had some sachets of lube in my bag and some condoms. Was I going to use a condom? I would see what he thought.

I poured a third large whiskey and coke and started taking his trousers off and going to work.

Mary Magdalene understood what I was doing. I was giving the world pleasure.

I started giving the best blowjob I could.

The next few hours were delightful. I teased and I tormented him. I became cruel. I became sensual. I became delicate. I became rough. I varied everything and every moment to play with this young man's brain and make him want me more. I had two spirits – I was the dominant she-male oppressor when he wanted it and the submissive girlfriend whore a few minutes later. As I took sex toys and my crucifix out of my bag I kissed him deep and hard like he had never been kissed before. When we finished I swallowed all his sperm and then I showed him the crucifix and explained to him how it symbolised my childhood on the Isle of Man. I don't mind looking back. I don't mind being a revisionist.

Around 6am he became anxious and said that he suddenly had to leave. He put his clothes on quickly. He left his socks on the bedroom floor and put his shoes on awkwardly and left without a kiss.

'I'll call a taxi for you.'

'I need to g-g-g-go. I am sorry. Th-th-th-thanks for a good time.'

And he left. He didn't even have my number. Was he a traitor like Judas Iscariot? No, he was just cowardly like Pontius Pilate.

And that was the end of it. I slept a few hours and then the butterfly Coco Louise derobed and became Jeff again for a Sunday of conformity and religion.

In the morning I visited the blessed Alan Turing statue off Whitworth Street – the man who was a hero to many in our gay community for what he gave to the world, yet how he was persecuted for his sexuality in his later life. I then bought a coffee and walked into my local church at 11am, where they were starting a Holy Communion service. He would never see me again, but I had had my fun and I had pulled a hotter boy than Tamzin for once and that would keep me satisfied until the following Friday.

I sat through the church service, the vicar's sermon and the hymns and the prayers from the Book of Common Prayer. I knelt down and took my weekly Holy Communion with the smell of anal lubricant and whiskey and coke in the air around me and the people in the congregation who were sat near me.

Transgender people may define as heterosexual, homosexual, bisexual or asexual. Transgender people may need counselling and mental health services to deal with the stigma and anxiety and depression they experience every week.

I am not Joanna Jet and I will never be Paris Lees. I am just an all-conquering spirit in a church on a Sunday morning who is nothing like anyone else around them. After I took my Holy Communion I sang my hymns as loudly as possible, knowing that Jesus loved me for the unique and pleasure-giving T-girl that I had become.

'Nice to see you, Jeff. I hope you have had a fulfilling weekend,' the vicar said to me as we drank coffee after the service.

I had indeed. I am Coco Louise and Coco Louise sparkles every weekend without fail.

A LONELY SHADOW

Which year in the Second World War was the bleakest? Which was the year that was the toughest to get through? It was 1942, because the death toll was high by then and there was no end in sight.

There was to be a top-secret demonstration of new high explosives and Clement had been invited to watch on. The welfare state and the NHS existed merely in this man's brain at the time.

Clement stood amongst a group of VIPs that included Winston, whose glittering political career began in inauspicious circumstances with a defeat in an Oldham by-election, on the high ground that was known as Spectator's Hill. Nearby there were deep trenches into which all the onlookers would be warned to retire two minutes before the detonation took place.

How many innocent people were killed in Hiroshima a few years later? How many were killed in Nagasaki? Were they less human to us because of their different race and the thousands of miles between us and them? Was this in fact the most horrible, vicious and unforgivable act of all, in that we were all complicit in it and none of us has ever really properly apologised?

The highest ranking officer running the operation sent

his man to the Prime Minister to ask for permission to proceed with the demonstration.

The young officer's lonely shadow walked past Clement and was just about to reach Winston when all hell broke loose – a premature explosion occurred.

It was a deafening blast which blew tin hats off and threw spectators to the ground. A dense cloud of suffocating black smoke and dust engulfed the group and Clement wheezed and coughed and choked.

As it cleared, spectators could be seen shamefacedly clambering out of the trenches.

The hillside was deserted.

Except for two figures. One was unconcernedly chewing a large cigar and the other was a lonely figure staring at him.

The shaken young officer came up to speak to them both:

'Quite a bang that.'

'Proves the stuff works,' said Winston pragmatically. 'This is just the start.'

Clement said nothing and his good nature was complicit in all that followed, the horror and the redemption.

PLEASE DON'T WEAR RED TONIGHT (PART ONE)

The River Mersey connects Manchester and Liverpool. Rival football teams and a lot of hatred over the years. I always feel that the two cities are like feuding siblings, vying for the nation's full affections. In the sixties I think it is fair to say that the 'pool of life' won the battle. No one has decided who has won the great war between them yet though...

There is a place where I think I can go, when I feel low...

I had always wanted to be away at sea. It's the best place for a guy like me. There is a mystery and magic to a sailor's life that grabbed me from a young age. I always used to like going down by the docks in Liverpool and talking to the old seamen about their adventures. They talked of exotic sirens and places that never aged. I guess the fact that I was brought up an orphan meant that I never really felt an attachment to a particular home or place. I wanted to be on the move all the time and I lusted for an uncertain future.

I went to the Bluecote School in Liverpool, which at that time took in orphan boys. I don't remember enjoying it much or learning much and every chance I had I would orientate towards the docks and my calling away at sea. What I used to love most was looking out to sea on bright blue-skied days and trying to figure out where the sky ended and where the sea began – that mysterious blurring of two similar colours represented the place I yearned to be, no one really knowing where one Freddie ended and another Freddie began.

I left a mundane office job at sixteen and went away to sea properly for the first time. This was my place. I became a bellboy and a waiter. I had plenty of charm and the gift of the gab. Rich folks particularly loved having me around. It was easy to impress them, it came naturally to me. I would roll on the compliments and the flattery and they would tip you well, but then combine it ever so slightly with a roguish sense of humour so that you stood out from the other servants as a bit of a rough diamond – I did this just enough that it awakened the naughtier sides of their personalities that had to stay relatively hidden in polite society. Oh, I was crafty, always have been, and so I used to make a tidy sum on the side as well. I was so good that they used to say that ships wouldn't leave Liverpool unless Freddie was on board.

My son was born during a heavy air raid on 9th October 1940 at 6:30am. Actually it was my old lady's sister that chose the name, but I liked the name all the same and went along with it. I met Julia out with all her mates one evening and she was a rare beauty – tall, leggy, elegant and wearing an incredible and eye-catching red dress (it is still her in the red dress that I can see in my mind if I close my eyes and think of a woman now). She was confident too and always had a sarcastic riposte for my one-liner putdowns.

To be honest this was what attracted me to her the most as it made her stand out from all the other Scouse girls. We weren't married when we had John and I was having one of my most wayward, rolling stone periods of my life. For a while I deserted ship and no one back in Liverpool knew where I was. I believe that Julia's sister took John and looked after him for this period. She was the more stable and reliable one and she always wanted him from the start. Like I said, she even named him to begin with. There were deep-seated jealousies and issues there between her and Julia that became deeper as the battle for John's attention grew over the years. I think, to be honest, that both myself and Julia wanted her sister to adopt him, but I am told that they could never get us down to the office at the same time to sign the right forms for that.

Anyway, so I had a bit of a wilderness period. The 'lost weekend', maybe you would call it, a bit like what I read that my son got up to in Los Angeles in the seventies when I was in Brighton and just starting to get really sick.

'Freddie, go and get drunk and miss your boat,' some of the lads said to me, I recall.

So I did. I was always good at stuff like that.

I hung out with some rare old birds and drank an awful lot of rum. I blacked out for a few days, I think, but the bits that I remember were great fun. A lot of dancing. A lot of loose women. I never slept with any of these women to be honest with you, I don't even think I ever kissed any of them, but when you are away at sea for weeks, maybe even months on end, there is a way that you can behave around the ladies of the sea that you could never get away with on dry land. You could raise a glass and toast the Titanic, the second coming, the end of the world, you name it. Oh boy, those nights were fun and the dry land bunch never experienced anything like it.

Anyway, it all led to me ending up being locked up on Ellis Island.

If I recall correctly, I always had an ambition to be the head waiter on the *Queen Mary*, but it didn't work out that way – my 'lost weekend' put an end to all that. It turned out I got marched onto a liberty ship heading for North Africa (I don't really remember this, but a friend of mine told me later on that year). When we arrived there I was falsely accused of something apparently and they put me in jail for three months. Three bloody months – it was awful! I thought my life was over. Liverpool days, a life at sea, a woman's touch, the taste of rum, they all seemed like things I would never experience again. I thought I was going to die in that fucking prison and I gave up hope of a future. Mentally, a part of me died in prison and never came back. Having said that, I did write some letters to Julia. I couldn't send any money, but I could write letters and letters are one of the most powerful things when you are at your lowest point. I wonder if Julia ever kept them.

When I eventually got out I wrote to her some more.

'There is a war on,' I remember saying to her. 'Go out and enjoy yourself.'

And she did. Too much though. She only went and forgot about me and got herself another man, did our Julia. Still, I suppose I can't blame her, knowing what I was like – never around, unreliable, drinking too much, no financial stability. I think it is fair to say that Julia was more sinned against than sinning.

A lot of time passed with me away at sea. The war was on and my schedule became more hectic and unpredictable. I hated Hitler and the Germans like everyone else and, if anything, that bloody war helped focus me on a cause again, helped remind me that I was basically a good person after all. I don't like people that are nasty to other people because of their race or background. I saw people doing similar things all the time on those ships in the early days. Talking nasty to someone because they were black or talking down to someone because they had less money than them. I always hated all that kind of behaviour. There are black arseholes, there are white arseholes and there are yellow arseholes. The only people I am racist against are arseholes. I believe John felt the same thing and I am proud to say he got that from me. He might not have got much else from me, the musical talent and good looks and all that were from his mum, but I am proud to say he got something from his old man.

So during one leave I decided to go and visit John and I took him to Blackpool. I think he was about five years old at the time. I actually intended to take him away then and never come back. He had a winning personality even at that age and I became very fond of him.

We went and stayed with a friend of mine. The war was over and I had been getting my head down and making bags of money, some legitimately, but, to be honest, a lot of it was black market stuff. I was on a lot of rackets, you couldn't go wrong in those days. They are probably still selling the stuff that I brought over in Blackpool now.

Anyway, so me and the little lad were getting on great guns, a real father and son bit of bonding. I was realising the things I liked about being a dad, that I had never thought of before or been too chicken scared to think of. We had fun down on the beach, taking in all the rides and I helped him indulge in all his imaginary worlds. He even started doing running commentaries of some of them. I would listen along and smile and then at the end of it I would adopt my best British Broadcasting Corporation accent and declare, 'If you liked that, come again next week, it'll be even better!' and we would both chuckle together.

My mate in Blackpool had been planning for some time now to emigrate to New Zealand. He talked about it all the time and he showed me letters and postcards that were very persuasive. I decided I was going to go as well and was going to take John with me. I was getting everything together and buying everything that the three of us would need to make the journey. Then out of the blue Julia showed up on my friend's doorstep. I wasn't expecting that. I was always a spontaneous person, who got up and moved and went where I wanted when the feeling took me. Married life was never going to be for me. I just liked to live a travelling sailor's life from one day to the next. I liked the roll of the waves, the power of the tides and the sea's ability to control me and make decisions for me. But on this day in Blackpool I had to make a big decision and John an even bigger one. This was the day and these were the moments that shaped everything that followed.

Julia was wearing red when she showed up that evening. She said she wanted John back. She had managed to settle down properly in a nice middle-class suburb and was controlling the manic side of her personality better than in his earliest years. She wanted him and I think she wanted to take him from her sister too because she was jealous, but I could just be speculating on that last point. The jealousies ran both ways with those too – her sister was jealous of Julia for her beauty and humour and free-spiritedness. Julia was equally jealous back, because her sister always had her shit together and was more successful and disciplined and better with money and the ways of the world than she was.

As I remember it I basically said that I was now so used to John that I was going to take him to New Zealand with me. But I could tell she really loved him and loved him a lot more than she loved me so I said to her that she should come along as well.

We could start all over again.

She said no without hesitation.

All that she wanted was John.

So we argued and argued, in a way that we had never argued before. The passions between us that day were stronger than we had ever experienced or known before. We weren't that passionate about each other but we found our passion through John.

'OK then,' I said. 'We should let John decide.'

I told John that he had to decide whether to stay with his dad and go to New Zealand or go back with his mum and live in Liverpool. I suppose it was an unfair thing to do to a five-year-old boy really. It felt like a big thing at the time, but as the years passed that moment became more and more monumental.

At first he jumped onto my knee and clung onto me hard. I had won the battle, I thought, and Julia started walking away in tears, knowing she was losing her son. But then suddenly when she was about thirty or forty yards away John let go of my leg and ran off after his mother. They embraced and she picked him up and carried him away. Neither of them looked back and they disappeared into the Blackpool fog. I stood still for a while and it felt like the right thing had happened. I didn't feel like I had lost. A boy deserves to be with his mother and an old rogue like me deserved to be on his own and on those waves again.

I married Pauline in Gretna Green when I was fifty-four. She was only eighteen, and none of her family came to the wedding. I heard that they all disapproved massively of my reputation and the age difference between us. In fact I don't think that there was a single thing about our relationship or the marriage that they did approve of. We lived happily down in Brighton, me and Pauline, but I asked her at an early stage to promise me that she would never wear red and she abided by that until my end days, bless her.

We had two sons, who were John's half-brothers, but he never met them. It was stomach cancer that got me and John sent me flowers from America. Of course, he had become one of the most famous men in the world by that point, a genius musician and songwriter and an icon of the counterculture. Me, I was a rolling stone, someone who had to be on the sea or near the sea to feel happy. I had an alright life. I wouldn't complain and I wouldn't do anything differently. I felt proud of John and was pleased for his success, although I never really knew him.

Would he have ended up like me if his aunt hadn't

have bought him that first guitar in Liverpool? Who knows. What would have happened if the two of us had ended up eloping from Blackpool to New Zealand? In an interview he did once say he might have ended up like me if he hadn't gone to art college. Maybe not.

PLEASE DON'T WEAR RED TONIGHT
(PART TWO)

Love your eyes over these words of truth, hopefully you will be uplifted.

Benjamin Zephaniah

I was always the stoic type, even when I was at primary school. I was practical and I wanted the best for good people. I hid my love away as much as possible and by burying it I created something that was intense and powerful. Only now can I open up and tell you about it. What I am going to tell you now about me and John and Julia will reveal everything I have suppressed all those years. He was the dreamer, she was the ocean child, but there are no poetic words to describe me. For the first time in my life I am using my imagination and creating. People say that imagination is more important than knowledge. This is my best shot at the prize. My stoic side disapproves, but I don't have long to live now.

John moved in with me and my husband George in Menlove Avenue in Woolton when he was too young to remember. I never told him about his mum and dad. I just wanted to protect the young lad and for him to be happy. History will always say that I was a disciplinarian and I suppose I was, but I never hit him or shouted at him like a lot of adults used to do in the post-war years.

George cared for him a lot too; don't anybody underestimate that.

'Dear George, will you take me to Woolton Pictures?'

And often he did. George was perfectly matched for me. He was calm and gentle and kind and he could read people and situations well. He probably should have been a detective or someone high up in the police. He understood that Julia was unstable and experienced extreme highs and lows. Yet he also understood that she was basically a good person with love for all of us. George helped glue everything together; he didn't panic or do anything irrational and he loved having a little lad around all the time. A lot changed when George died. Tempers became fraught, I was less calm and I think it led to Julia being more irrational and trespassing onto my patch more with her rebellious and rock and roll ways. George had a calming effect on the relationship I had with my sister. I really miss him and I was never with another man after he died of a brain haemorrhage. John was thirteen, I believe, when this happened. People said that I should have tried to find someone else after George died, but I think you only have one big love in your life and if I had got with another man I would have been being unfaithful to George and unfaithful to myself. Some people will never really understand that, I don't think. I'm not like everybody else.

I used to particularly love taking John to Strawberry Fields, the local Salvation Army children's home. Each summer they used to have a big garden party and lots of other boys his age used to go as well. John only ever really mixed with them if he was able to create a gang or be the leader of that gang. That was always in his nature and I saw it clearly in his relationships with other boys his age. But some of those boys in Strawberry Fields didn't take to being in a gang and I think John could sense that. So I remember that he used to just walk around the place and drift between the crowds, always observing and always acutely aware of everything that was going on around him.

Growing up, money didn't mean anything to John and he was always generous beyond belief if he had any. I wouldn't really say that he got that from me. I was always more cautious with money. I wasn't tight or stingy, just careful and prudent and practical – with money and with everything really.

'The guitar is alright, John, but you'll never make a living out of it.'

One of the biggest things I remember about those primary school years and Julia's continued absence (she would just show up when it suited her) was all the imaginary worlds and characters that John would create. He used to get really excited about these worlds of his. I still have a scrapbook collection that he used to have called 'Sport, Speed and Illustrated' – I think he put it together when he was about seven. There were sporting characters based on the worlds of *Alice in Wonderland* and *The Wind in the Willows*. These characters used to have races against each other, play football matches against each other, or just go off on the maddest of adventures. And each chapter used to end with, 'If you like this, come again next week, it'll be even better.' Goodness knows who he thought he was speaking to, but he had these audiences in his head, even from the earliest years.

Most people used to think he was my son and to be fair I never used to correct them when they said this. The truth is that I wanted him to be my son and I wanted Julia to stay away. Yet just when I felt I had him all to myself, that was exactly when Julia would come waltzing back into his life with her corrupting influences. I would lose him to her at these moments and feel so much jealousy about this. I hated myself for feeling like that. Why should I deny a boy the opportunity to spend time with his mother; it's a natural thing you would think? But I knew too well that Julia just showed up when it suited her and laughed and flirted with his friends as he became a rebellious teenager. It was so dangerous for him; she could undo a lot of the years of patience and manners I had put into him in just one afternoon. She could then just disappear again because of one of her mood swings and leave him feeling lost and confused. People said she was bipolar and the problem with Julia's erratic behaviour was that she could leave John confused and disappointed when she would cancel on him.

When he was old enough to get in gangs I remember walking down Penny Lane one time and seeing a big fight between a group of adolescent lads. It was one of those scenes you wanted to avoid and felt ashamed of. As the crowd of lads dissipated I saw John in the centre of the melee with a torn school shirt and bruises and blood on his face. I couldn't believe it. I rushed over and hugged him tight. He hugged me back and said he was sorry for causing the fight and that I had seen it. He told me that older boys had been picking on him and one of his friends and so he felt he had to defend himself and his friend. I believed everything John told me, he was brutally honest – always.

Oh please don't keep coming over to Menlove Avenue, Julia.

Please don't keep showing up unannounced and connecting with him in a way that I am unable to.

Please don't bring him all of your musical presents.

Please don't teach him to stray away from me.

Please don't wear red tonight.

Please don't take my boy away from me.

He is my boy now.

Yet he is drawn to you always, the ocean child.

He ran away from Freddie in Blackpool to be with you.

He may run away from me at any point too.

I have lost George.

God, don't let her take John away from me too.

She lived five to ten miles away, but her visits became more regular as he was becoming a man and becoming lost to music. He had his own proper gang by then and those vague memories of his past and those unanswered questions were rising into his consciousness – ammunition for creativity, but also food for insecurity and primal scream treatment.

Julia came to see him one day around the time that he was at Quarry Bank High School in Allerton. She was wearing a black coat, with her face all bleeding. She'd had some sort of accident and had a shocked look on her face. I couldn't face it. Yet she went straight to John when this happened. The bond was so strong, particularly when either of them were feeling emotionally vulnerable. In many ways she became more like a big sister to him.

'She did everything for laughs. Just like us,' one of his gang once said. 'She'd wear a pair of spectacles with no glass in, and then go up to people on the street and start talking to them. Then she would put her finger through the space where the glass should be and start scratching her eye.'

And the rows and arguments between me and him would increase during these periods as I tried to protect him. Yet he wanted to rebel and be more like his mother and spend more time with his big-sister mother.

She helped make him a rebel. She spoke the same language as him. Liked the same things, hated the same sort of people.

He failed all his O-levels and then got into art college. I guess that place was full of all the types of creative maverick characters he was thriving off. Girls who dressed like Brigitte Bardot or men who thought they were beatniks and existentialists. He drank down Ye Cracke and became obsessed with skiffle and Elvis Presley. I remembered that Julia played the banjo and I couldn't play anything. I never had that kind of talent; it just wasn't in me. And the jealousy rose up inside me so much at this time. And I hated myself for it. And I lost him as much as I have ever lost him. It was the worst time of my life and the effects of George's death reared up in my head more at this time too. And there was nothing I could do about it.

The copper came to the door and told us about the accident. First thing he did was speak to John and ask him if he was her son. I can still remember it like it was yesterday.

It was the 15th July 1958.

The accident happened near my house.

She had been hit by a car when going to the bus stop.

They say there was a terrible screeching.

I never told people the exact spot even though I knew it. It was somewhere they walked every day. It would have been too harrowing to tell.

She was lying dead at Sefton General.

How did John react? I remember him shouting at me 'Fuck it. Fuck it. That's really fucked everything. I've no responsibility to anyone now.'

Then I think he buried his emotions, but they would come out at different times. I heard that a girlfriend once said to him angrily, 'Don't take it out on me because your mother's dead.'

I knew that he still loved me and we grew closer again. He grew close to Paul as well because of their shared mother's deaths, but he found it hard to understand why Paul didn't get as upset as he did when he talked about it. He became more cruel at this time too I think – cruel drawings, cartoons of the Pope dying, deformed babies, a Hieronymus Bosch obsession. Liverpool was full of deformed people and somehow he became obsessed with it all.

Of course, he then went on to have close relationships with Stuart and Cynthia that helped fill the hole that Julia had left. I never felt any jealousy towards these people – I liked them. We stayed very close and he called me most weeks when he moved away. Of course, I was very proud of everything he went on to achieve. But what would have happened if Julia hadn't have died? She wore a summer dress that evening in July and there was blood everywhere. The dress turned red with all the blood as the copper walked towards our house and the ambulance people arrived on the scene. Did I want Julia to die? Did I cause Julia's death? Did I get John back after that tragic day? Maybe. Maybe not.

REDEMPTION SONG

Time has a beginning and time has an ending. Don't let anyone fool you that we live in infinity. Your life matters. You get one shot at it. Don't lose it. Make it count.

I remember when I was first diagnosed. I went down onto the beach when the tide was as far out as it would go. I stared and stared at the relentless monotony of the waves. Who was it that controlled their repetitive precision and who was it that ensured they would never stop? I had said thank you to the doctor for his time earlier in the day and we had arranged our next appointment. After the beach I went back into town and lost myself in unusual street names, walking for long periods of time with my eyes closed and spinning myself to dizziness on street corners in the dark. It would possibly have made my task easier if I had strayed out and been hit by a car and died there and then.

I spent days and evenings like this, trying to come to terms with the fact that I was going to die soon. I slept rough and went through periods of not contacting anyone. I had taken the test to give my life a boost, to remind myself of how lucky I was and, although I had put it off for years, I was confident that I would be fine. Then suddenly all of my life was in ruins. So many of the day-to-day things that you took for granted seemed pointless. Why should I bother each day about my personal appearance? I was going to be a rotting carcass soon and so many things seemed pointless. Money was just bits of paper. I had no desire for new friends and I made no plans beyond the present. I knew that I had the power to put myself out of this misery whenever I wanted to.

It was my brother who brought me back to life. He had taken his two children into town on a Saturday afternoon and driven back home in the early evening, when he saw a familiar figure lying flat on his back at the entrance to his gravel drive. It was a cold October evening in Didsbury and my trousers were wet through. By this point I had become accustomed to sleeping rough and was uninterested in any pedestrians walking by. Luke saw my lifeless eyes and told me to wait there until he had taken my nephew and niece inside of the house. Naturally he didn't want them seeing their uncle in such a state. I remember that he started to cry when I told him everything and he wasn't the crying type. He was actually the first person I had told everything to as I had been burying my feelings away up until that point.

'Why didn't you contact me?' he asked. 'We are close. We used to tell each other everything.'

'I haven't told anyone. I think I had to let myself get to grips with it first.'

'OK, well, you can stay here with me for now.'

I said thank you, but I also remember saying that everything was not going to be OK and that what I had was incurable.

'I am dying,' I said with emphasis.

He knew.

I stayed in the spare room and Luke kept me busy. I helped with the shopping and cooking and spent time with my nephew and niece. Jamie was eight years old and fanatical about football. We had epic Manchester derbies in the garden and penalty shoot-outs with over-excited running commentaries. Jade was equally enthusiastic about life and was always trying to keep up with her elder brother or behave like a tomboy. Their naivety and appetite for life helped to make me feel a little better.

I went to the clinic on a regular basis. I saw a counsellor once a week and was also part of an evening collective of people that met up and discussed the hell they were going through. I got angry with Luke at times, because I felt that I needed more or less pity, depending on my mood. I was sorry for this; I never meant to upset him.

Some nights I just sat out in the park and looked at the stars. Some mornings I simply sat on a bench and watched people doing part of their daily commute into work. Everyone looked so robotic, as if they had no idea what they had been put on this earth for.

It was on that bench on Wilmslow Road that I had the revelation. Watching the commuting robots one morning made me decide how I wanted the rest of my life to be. Instead of spending a life in jobs, careers and relationships that I didn't want to be in, I was going to cram as much joy, fun and excitement into the last six months of my life as I possibly could. I decided that I was going to do all of the things that I really wanted to do with my life but had hesitated over in the past because of the fear of the unknown or the fear of failure. Suddenly, being terminally ill felt like the best thing that had ever happened to me. It made me focused and efficient and stopped me from wasting my time as I had so often in the past. I realised that my lack of time gave me the motivation that I needed to do things for myself and for other people too.

I sold the majority of material possessions that I owned over the next few weeks. I decided to give a certain amount of the money I had to charity. I researched thoroughly and picked out the charities that moved me the most. I wanted to help disabled people and children that were born with little hope or prospects for the future. I wanted to know that my money would genuinely make a difference and so I read through all the websites and the case studies and the pie charts of where the money went. After I had made these arrangements I decided that it was time to have some fun.

I booked a round-the-world ticket and set off on my adventures. I had never been as excited in my life as I was when my plane left the ground from Manchester Airport. I had flown and been on many holidays before, but I had never really savoured it. In the past there had always been an inner-voice telling me that I would be happier tucked up in my cosy English bedroom. On this trip though I was determined to squeeze every bit of enjoyment out of it that I could. I went on a safari in Africa, travelled to Zanzibar, island hopped in Thailand, trekked across *Lord of the Rings* country in New Zealand, went to great sporting events and rock concerts in Australia, and then planned an epic road trip across America, taking in the great musical cities of Chicago, Nashville, Memphis and New Orleans. Everywhere exceeded my expectations and

I met so many memorable people too. These people had always been there, in my line of vision, but I guess I had never properly reached out to them before and asked them questions. It was the build-up to the big Hillary Clinton and Donald Trump election and everywhere I went I asked people their views and soaked up their backgrounds, experiences and world views. I took the attitude that every day could be my last. I tackled everything I did with an enthusiasm that had been sadly lacking from the rest of my life. This enthusiasm was infectious and I noticed how people started liking me more than they had in the past. I noticed this really vividly because I had never been that popular before. Sometimes I felt an urge to talk to other travellers about my condition, but I made the decision not to. It meant that there were many farewells that included plans to meet up in the future that would never happen. There were many new Facebook friends who would one day notice that I had vanished mysteriously from their lives. But what is Facebook anyway? It can dominate your life. Johnny Cash and Joe Strummer were never on Facebook. One day in New Orleans towards the end of my great world trip and as I was soaking up the colours and tastes and spectacles of the Mardi Gras I decided to deactivate my account permanently.

When I finally came home my body was starting to give out warning signs. Like Freddie Mercury when he was recording his last albums, I guess. My life was reaching a closure period and I had a feeling of contentment to go with it. I felt good about the money that was going to charity, about my great trip and about my new closeness with my family. Everything was falling into place. My life had meaning to it and I was going to die having made the world a better place, which I probably wouldn't have said a few years before.

With my last two grand I threw a big party before my final trip to the clinic. I was frail and weak at this point, but I felt like being lavish and indulgent. I gathered together all of my closest friends. I took drugs, I danced all night and I had a threesome with two escort girls that a friend of mine had ordered in. I was ready to die now and in a hungover state I made my way over to the clinic for the very last time.

Luke drove me there that day and we were both fighting back the tears. We shared a lot of brotherly love on that journey, but I told Luke to stay calm; this was how everything was supposed to be.

My doctor came into the room dressed as usual but with a surprisingly broad smile considering the occasion.

'Mr Salewicz. We have some news we need you to hear.'

'Sure. Go for it.'

'Immunologists in California have made a major breakthrough in recent weeks. We believe that you can now be totally cured.'

I looked at the photographs of the beach on the clinic wall. The waves looked threatening and dangerous and the beach seemed unprepared for them. The sky above the waves had been photographed at sunset so as to intensify the dark blue of the sea. I stared and stared at the photograph, imagining what it would be like to be on that beach. What should I do now? Where should I go from here? I wanted to die.

THE GIRL WITH THE NAZI TATTOO

She had fake breasts and pink hair. Not when I first interviewed her, actually. When I first interviewed her she had blue hair. I remember that she was pretty, but she came and went out of my life quickly. The second time she came into my life her hair had changed colour and she had had the breast implants. They looked good and all the men I knew couldn't take their eyes off her. I often wondered why girls got breast implants, but it now made a lot more sense to me – she was able to be the centre of attention instantly and be loud and engaging without actually saying anything interesting or engaging. The men loved her. I think she pissed a lot of the girls off.

'Stop touching my fake boobs,' she said loudly and jokingly many times that evening, so as many people as possible could hear.

We talked more in the pub the second time and we discovered a love of the same music, the same punk bands of years ago.

She had lots of tattoos and was actually a part-time tattoo artist. I would love to see some of her drawings, I told her. She clearly had talent. I was a writer, I told her, and so maybe we should combine our talents. She could illustrate some of my stories, I suggested. Sounds sleazy doesn't it? I didn't mean it that way at the time. I just think we had a connection in the pub that evening on the second occasion that we properly met.

Later that evening my friend Joe kept saying to me, 'I can't stop thinking about Michelle's breasts.'

'Ha ha, she has a boyfriend, I think. I can't stop thinking about her tattoos,' I responded and didn't give the matter much further thought as we embarked on our early hours of the morning adventures that led to circling roundabouts in the pouring rain and staying up all night in Salford bedsits.

Two years passed by.

I moved abroad and came home. And there Michelle was one evening, working behind the bar at a lively old man's pub that served no food except for the best Victoria Sponge cake and, at certain times of the year, the newly invented Manchester Egg.

We reconnected like old lovers and I started frequenting that pub more and more. I would pop my head in on the way home from work most days. If she was working I would take a seat at the bar and have a few drinks. If she wasn't I would go to the toilets and then leave without making eye contact with anyone.

Sitting at the bar and watching her work led to me falling in love with her. I loved watching the way she interacted with the other customers, from the older regulars, to the wannabe hipsters, to the ruder and drunker clientele. Her command of the bar space was consummate and magnetising. Like Bruce Springsteen's stagecraft throughout a four-hour concert, she knew exactly when to interact with me (to keep me interested), when to flirt, when to back off, when to be loud, when to be quiet, when to question and when to command and dominate.

'Tell me more about your tattoos,' I asked her. I had two and was eager to show them off. She had fifteen and said she only wanted to reveal them to me one at a time.

I told my old friend Joe that I had found Michelle again and was drinking at the pub that she worked at. He looked startled and nervous, and not as excited as I thought. I wanted to know why.

'Did I never tell you about her Nazi tattoo?'

'No. What Nazi tattoo?'

'Well, I worked with her a lot for a few weeks after that night. You remember, the night when you talked to her constantly in the pub and I became fixated with her fake breasts.'

'And...'

'I don't know why I didn't tell you this at the time, it must have slipped my mind. She has this tattoo on her left shoulder that says "Bound For Glory".'

'So? So what? A Woody Guthrie song? Part of a Bruce Springsteen lyric?'

'No mate. Her dad was in a band called Bound For Glory, a punk band. You know how much she likes her punk rock?'

I nodded.

'Well, her dad was the drummer, but he died when Michelle was just eleven and so she got the tattoo to remind her of him. Quite sweet really, I guess. The thing is though I decided to research the band a bit, because she said they were quite famous, yet I hadn't heard of them at all. It turns out they were a white supremacist band, a

Nazi punk band basically with some horrible racist songs and lyrics. You can find some of their songs on YouTube. But I believe that the music press have largely ignored or boycotted them because of their fascist principles and following. It put me off her. I didn't talk to her much after that.'

After speaking with Joe I wanted to find out more. It seemed implausible to me that this highly attractive, alternative and intelligent young girl living in the heart of one of the most liberal cities in the world could have racist views. Joe's story had drawn me in and I became more fascinated by her than before. I kept drinking at her pub and talking and flirting with her like before, but I didn't bring up the Bound For Glory tattoo.

She told me she had a boyfriend she had been going out with for about a year. His name was Steve, but it wasn't really working out – they were arguing all the time, she said. It seemed like she was on the brink of breaking up with him, but was unlikely to make the first move herself.

I had a Saturday night out with friends a few weeks after my discussion with Joe and returned to my apartment around 2am. Michelle started texting me.

'What are you doing tonight? I want to see you.'

She said she was finishing up at the pub, but was living a nocturnal lifestyle and wanted to keep on drinking. She wanted to keep on drinking with me specifically. So I texted her my address and she came round to mine about 3am.

The next two hours were about as much fun as I can recall having at that time in the morning.

She had brought a bottle of flavoured vodka with her

and we drank and talked. Fast-paced and impassioned conversations about our lives and the music sound tracking them. I kept changing the CDs, picking the best punk songs I could that weren't necessarily the obvious ones and became more and more frenzied and excited as the guitar chords and vodka flowed.

She put on one of my hats and straddled me on the sofa and started kissing me without any inhibitions.

Leaving a CD playing loud, we rushed through to the bedroom and ripped each other's clothes off. Neither of us had the time for foreplay and we had punk rock sex in my bed. Fast, loud, no solos, no unnecessary noises, lots of mistakes, but no shame in the mistakes. These moments were raw and unplanned. Finally we fell asleep in each other's arms.

When I woke up I saw the tattoo that Joe had told me about and it said 'Bound For Glory' in large black ink on her left shoulder.

'So, tell me more about your other tattoos. The ones you haven't told me about before.'

She talked and talked.

Some were drawings of shipwrecks.

Some were Japanese symbols.

Some were song lyrics that she loved.

She talked about fourteen out of the fifteen tattoos that she had on her body and then she started talking about her dad rather than the fifteenth tattoo.

I was anti-racist, anti-fascist and a signed-up member of Unite Against Fascism. Naturally I was scared inside of what she was going to say next. Had I betrayed all my ideals that night? Had I started to love the thing I hated?

She talked more and more about her dad – what a popular guy he was, how everyone in her village held a memorial service each year to mark his passing. How he was an amazing father, who Michelle and her younger sister had both idolised. How he had been in a great punk rock band that had a huge following in Lancashire – with the boots and braces skinhead crowd. But how he was only in this band for their seminal debut album and then left for mysterious reasons that he never fully explained to his daughters. He spent the rest of his life working as a part-time postman and a drumming teacher.

'You'd have loved him,' she whispered in my ear as we lay naked next to each other in the morning.

'And he would have approved of you and everything that you do. I wish the two of you could have met.'

Michelle snuggled herself tightly into my wiry morning body and fell back asleep. She still had a boyfriend to break up with and I still had a whole lot more to learn about her.

WITHNAIL AND YOU

I am writing this one for you specifically. You with the book in your hand now. This one is from the heart and specifically for you, my falling friend. Are you suffering for your insanity? I hear that you like a few drinks, you have even considered (but never completed) the Withnail and I drinking game. Is this true? Perhaps once you have read this you will listen closer. I am writing this one for you specifically. You are too beautiful for this world of pain.

'We have just run out of wine. What are we going to do about it?'

I made it to my thirties and might still make it to my forties, but I drink more with each passing year. It tastes damn good and it takes me away from reality. Reality is horrible and I don't want anything to do with it – I am not good enough, I don't have the talent, nobody loves me. Dealing with those realities sober became unbearable in my twenties, but with alcohol I can make those feelings go away and I enjoy the feeling of excitement that comes with the next drink and the rollercoaster ride of conversation and magical circumstances that tend to happen thereafter.

'You never discuss your family, do you?'

'We're incompatible. They don't like me being on stage.'

'Then they must be delighted with your career – you rarely are.'

Both my parents represent old-school England. They went to the top private schools and believe in the structures and hierarchies of the old-fashioned English class system. Their lives are drenched in snobbery and false etiquette and the stiff upper lip. Problems and emotions are to be swept under the carpet. Acting is pretending to them and they have no interest in it. I do not love my parents anymore and they do not love me.

Look at your watch now or the time on your phone. How many hours until opening time exactly? Don't do it. Don't follow me down this road. A road that leads to a rifle filled with red wine.

'We have got to get some booze. It is the only solution for this intense cold.'

'I am a trained actor reduced to the status of a bum.'

'Why can't I have an audition? I've been to drama school. I am good looking.'

For years and years I deluded myself that I had an abundance of acting talent. I know now that I am only good at acting that I have acting talent. I am good at pretending to be pretending. I can't handle the cold reality of it all. I can't remember lines and I get nervous and I get stage fright. The only audiences I recall now are cold and uninviting. I tried to get a cigar commercial one time, but even that fell through.

I am speaking directly to you now. Don't delude yourself about talent like I did. I surrounded myself with talented friends to mask my own inadequacies. Don't do that. Just surround yourself with real friends. You want to know what a real friend is? Imagine you are facing a potential jail sentence – see who sticks by you then and who doesn't.

So I drank and drank and drank...

'Two large gins. Two pints of cider – ice in the cider.'

And I moved further away from my parents and their money and into a life of squalor and hardship.

And I became more and more of a coward. All alcoholics are cowards to some extent. They are scared of reality. They are scared of their own failings. They are scared of their friends' successes. Is that you? Do you ever feel that?

And then you start lying more and more (but this is mainly lying without realising it). It just makes life more interesting and more exciting. You can create your own dramas and conspiracies to liven up the pub talk and the five pints down debates.

The hangovers all roll into one. You need a drink to get rid of the hangover, to get rid of the drink that got rid of the hangover, that got rid of the lie, that got rid of the life that might be left inside you.

'I've got a bastard behind the eyes.'

'I feel like a pig shat in my head.'

I suppose happiness is relative and I have had a fair few great times and great stories with my talented eccentric group of go-getting friends. We could live like a gang, but one by one they moved on. One by one they got married or one by one they became successful and moved away from me and my drunken influences. I never had that kind of grip on the girls; it was the young men that I could dazzle and mesmerise (for a while) and then I would lose them and have to find younger replacements. I thought about changing my name to Desmond Wolf or Donald Twain, but these were just whims to disguise the fact that I was going nowhere.

Are you going nowhere?

Or are you going to move on and leave me once you have finished reading this story? I am paranoid that you are and that I won't be able to hold your attention much longer.

Unless you are a romantic addict like me.

Happiness is relative for sure and I am getting a jolt of it now from interacting with you and watching you turn the pages. I think you have more talent than me and are also better looking. But will you be able to grip people for short periods of time like I can? I can hold people's attention for the duration of a poem or a short story or a rant or a drunken night on the town. I can't write novels. I can't do long-term relationships. I push women away and my friends all leave me in the end, one by one. They do their wild crazy sowing of oats years, tell me they will make a blood oath, and then fuck off to the middle of the road for the rest of their lives. This is Withnail talking. This is Withnail talking to you, my beautiful and holy friend.

'We are bona fide. We are not from London.'

'Understudy Constantine. I am not going to understudy Constantine. Why can't I play the part?'

I chose not to compromise and I drove my life as far away from the middle of the road as possible and into the ditch.

'You don't want to go to Manchester. Play a bloody soldier?'

I was incapable of the graft or the hard work that requires you to get ahead in life. I was incapable of indulging in anything but pleasure.

'You'll all suffer. I am going to be a star.'

But I never became a star and other people I interacted with didn't suffer like I thought they might. Around me people blossomed and grew and had great successes. Just like you – you are the hero of this short tale. You are beautiful and you have made it to the end, maybe learned a few things not to do in your life and kept me happy for a short while in my aging condition that has rejected suicide. Thanks for listening; you have given me back a little of my mirth.

THE BOY IN THE BUBBLE (PART TWO)

I am still a narcoleptic and I still have lucid dreams. Just in case you forgot, this means that I keep falling asleep all the time, without warning, and when I dream I am actually aware that I am dreaming. This helps me to survive the cold realities of my life. Most of the time I want to escape the person that I am. I am a prisoner in my own skin. I love the time I spend asleep – my life tends to fall apart for the periods when I am awake.

My stutter has also been getting worse lately, making me the nerviest and least confident black man that you will have ever met. I have retreated from all aspects of the student life around me. I like to be alone in my room, where I can put my head on the pillow and drift away…

The house of my dreams sounds like it is fairly full tonight. I walk through the wide front door and hang up my coat and hat in the usual way. Straight away I hear a booming and commandeering voice in the living room and I enter, drawn in by the charisma of the red-faced man in the centre of the room. One of the guys on the sofa looks up and smiles at me.

'Morning, Elliott.'

'H-h-h-hi, hi.'

I give him a thumbs up and he responds in kind, but

113

then looks back to the centre of the room to the leader who has everyone's attention.

'Well, I might as well tell you now. You lot may all be internationals and have won all the domestic honours there are to win under Don Revie. But as far as I'm concerned, the first thing you can do for me is to chuck all your medals and all your caps and all your pots and all your pans into the biggest fucking dustbin you can find, because you have never won any of them fairly. You've done it all by bloody cheating.'

I decided to leave the room for a while. The atmosphere was tense and awkward. I am not sure that the man doing all the talking was getting the kind of response he wanted from all the lads in the living room. I went to the kitchen and made myself a hot chocolate. Then after some more commotion the centre-of-attention man joins me with a drained demeanour.

'Did you hear that, Elliott?'

'Y-y-y-yeah, I d-d-d-did.'

'What those lads don't understand is that I won't eat and I won't sleep until I have taken what that man has achieved and beaten it. Beaten it, so that I never have to hear the name Don-fucking-Revie again. Beat it so that the only name anyone sings in the Yorkshire ale houses, raising their stinking jars to their stinking mouths, is Brian Clough. Brian-fucking-Clough uber-fucking-alles!'

I nod at this raging man and he gives me a sparkling wink.

'Good lad. Now I am taking my wife and kids to the pictures tonight. Keep the boys happy when I am gone, Elliott. You'll do that for me, won't you?'

I nod and wink back at him, he rubs his hands together excitedly and then leaves by the front door.

I decide that I need a quieter part of the house and so I ascend the stairs with my hot chocolate, too hot to drink properly yet. I walk into one of the main bedrooms and see a man with long dark hair and leather trousers sitting on the bed in meditation. I know him well and immediately feel at ease to sit on the edge of the bed next to him.

'You need to expose yourself to your deepest fear, Elliott. After that you will find that fear has no power. The fear of freedom will shrink and vanish. You will become free.'

'B-b-b-b-but I can't. I am sc-sc-sc-sc-scared.'

'I know but you need to get up on a stage and perform in front of people to realise your power and talent. At first I used to perform with my back to the audience, but then I confronted my fear and I became free.'

This mystical poet draped across the bed was asking a narcoleptic stutter-ridden social outcast to perform on stage. I loved his braveness and belief in the good of people. I guess he was right when he said that a friend is someone who gives you total freedom to be yourself. Leaning forward towards me and staring hard into my eyes, he continued softly.

'Don't listen to the crowds of men downstairs or the ones swirling around you through your unique life. I like people who shake other people up and make them feel uncomfortable.'

This reminded me of what I had just seen downstairs, but I smiled at the thought that the mystical poet in front of me was unlikely to have had much experience of a stinking Yorkshire ale house.

The poet lay back on the bed and looked upwards. He seemed to be lost in transcendental meditation and very quietly I heard the words, 'This is the strangest life I have ever known.'

I drank some of my hot chocolate and walked to the door. As I opened it to walk out, the poet on the bed spoke one last sentence at me – 'There are things known and things unknown and in between are the doors.'

I stood on the landing for a while and felt so excited by what was going on around me in this house of my lucid dreams. Elliott, I said to myself, you can draw inspiration from all of this, from what is around you and put the best elements of it into your own life. I felt like I was bolder than ever before and I turned towards the entrance to the other main bedroom on that floor. There stood in the doorway was an athletic figure with a worried look on his face.

'Good to see you, Elliott. It's been too long. There has been a lot of madness in the house recently. You need to come here more often. I think you help calm some of us down.'

'Hi, H-H-H-Harold. How you b-b-b-been?'

And we talked a little to each other calmly. Like the mystical poet, Harold knew Paris, but for very different reasons. My stutter became less pronounced with Harold because he put me at ease and was probably the most normal and conventional person in my boy in the bubble house. Despite this he too was an outsider and had those shattering moments of self-doubt just like me. We liked to discuss this in depth.

'I have ten lonely seconds to justify my whole existence, Elliott.'

I try to reassure him that there is more to his life than that, but he won't have any of it.

'I have never known happiness,' he tells me. 'I'm forever in pursuit and I don't even know what I am chasing. I have known the fear of losing but there are also times when I am too frightened to win. I need to have courage, Elliott – courage is grace under pressure.'

He pauses for a while then grabs me by both shoulders and the sense of calm that we just had has gone.

'Elliott, I am an addict for running, you see. It's compulsion for me. It's a weapon I can use. A weapon against being Jewish, I suppose.'

He tells me that he has a race tomorrow so is planning on putting the ear plugs in and getting an early night. He hopes that the others in the house keep the noise down tonight.

'Stay the night, Elliott. They will behave themselves if they know that you are back.'

I say good night to my friend and finish my hot chocolate. There is only the attic to go to now and my body trembles with excitement and anticipation at seeing the last guest of the house again. I know that he will be up there. I feel his presence, hiding away from the law, as I climb each flight of stairs and open up the old door. There he is sitting on the floor, muscles bulging, brooding and reading a book in his tight musty green T-shirt. He symbolises rock and roll in a time before rock and roll was born – his appearance is the vision of angels telling the truth to me in this heaven-like attic. He is the maddest guy in the world and obsessed with getting his kicks.

Kicks kicks kicks.

He puts his book down and starts talking to me like a maniac.

'Elliott, we gotta go and never stop going until we get there.'

'W-w-w-where to, m-m-m-man?'

'I don't know but we gotta go.'

He stands up and starts striding wildly around the dark room and soliloquising. I watch on gripped by this outlaw figure.

'The only people for me are the mad ones, the ones who are mad to live, mad to talk, mad to be saved, desirous of everything at the same time, the ones who never yawn or say a commonplace thing. We can be like this together, Elliott, my holy friend. Together we can burn, burn, burn, like fabulous yellow Roman candles, exploding like spiders across the stars.'

He talks more and more frantically and demoniacally and seraphically and circles me in the room, making me dizzier and dizzier. He tells me that the road is life and that sex is the one and only holy and important thing for him and that he has to get to Denver soon to see Marylou, but that first me and him will go to California – his California, which he tells me is wild, sweaty and important and the land of the lonely and eccentric lovers he has known.

'Come with me, Elliott,' he says as he keeps circling and I become dizzier and dizzier. 'Come with me.'

My dizziness intensifies, objects around me become a blur and soon all of my vision is lost.

I wake up in my student bed in Owen's Park and it is dark outside. I pull my curtains closed and pour myself a glass of water from the sink. I must go to dinner and face the world of my university halls and the apathetic and distant faces I see around me every day. I feel inferior again. Queueing up for my dinner in silence and surrounded by groups of noisy acquaintances and I am back in the real world again and I hate it. 'Expose yourself to your deepest fear,' the mystical poet had told me, but I don't know if I know how to, and therefore if I can ever do this. For now the characters in my dreams keep me warm and I am happy to remain the boy in the bubble.

LOOKING FOR THAT GLIMPSE OF TRUTH

I was blind for many years. I was often terrified to leave my own house and I had to depend heavily on my other senses to get me through life. My guide dog was like a saviour to me and gave me some independence and self-worth and staved off the loneliness and self-pity that kept gnawing at me in my private hours.

After years of blindness my sight came back to me this year. I now enjoy long and solitary walks through the city streets and I observe the little things as closely as possible and try to write them down with a pen and notebook in the pocket of my green jacket. I like observing the simple things and looking for a glimpse of truth in things I see and things that busy people probably miss every day, as they are focused on getting home to their wives and husbands or rushing to be on time for work. I don't have those things to distract me. I just have my Robin Hood blood sister to talk to every day, with her short spiky hair and desire to make the world a better place, a southerner originally but at home in the North like me – she is my inspiration and my muse. She makes me want to be a better person every day.

I walked through the centre of town today and down Market Street. The sky was completely grey and there was moisture in all of the air around me. It set itself into my face and beard and helped me feel more alive than ever. It was a Friday afternoon. The best time of the week. Everyone around me seemed to have a frenetic energy and an excited anticipation for something that was going to be happening to them over the next two days. I could feel the magic all around me as I strode under the Arndale Centre, heading in the direction of Piccadilly Gardens. At first I had a purple hoodie on with a leather jacket over the top of it, but as I walked on I took the leather jacket off and folded it over my arm.

There were Christians and Muslims and atheists and socialists, all with their own stands on the street and distributing their leaflets to put their points of view across to the unconverted. I took a few of the leaflets and learnt some new things about the teachings of Muhammad and some of the terrible things that our government (and others) were funding in far-off lands. I wanted to be an activist and I wanted to help in whatever way I could. I stood and talked for five minutes to a girl from the *Socialist Worker* newspaper and liked her immensely. Then I walked on past a talented busker singing Neil Young's 'Heart Of Gold' and the song's lyrics resonated more with me than ever before. The singer was young, but his voice was gravelly and had a world-weary quality to it.

The volume of people on the streets was enormous as darkness started to descend and the November evening began to set in. I stood still for a while, feeling the rush of energy around me and feeling dazzled by the pace of the traffic. The Christmas shopping period had begun and shops displayed bargains and special deals. Christmas songs were everywhere around me. I thought of my old guide dog, Bruce, and how he would have coped so calmly with a day like today. I resolved myself to be more like him.

As I reached Piccadilly Gardens I saw the yellow jackets of four young charity fundraisers asking passersby to make regular monthly donations to Marie Curie Cancer Care. I watched until all four of them were in conversation with strangers at once and then all four of them had their iPads out and were signing people up. I smiled and walked on, over towards the fountain and the group of restaurants at the corner of the Gardens. The whole city centre world appeared to me to be like an enormous theatre. I walked on past the old Piccadilly Rats, men in their fifties bashing out old rock and roll hits to a delighted crowd, transfixed by the wacky dancing old men at the front. I went and stood close to the fountain, where young children played and where water soared into the air and descended dramatically onto the cold stone ground. The young children were free from their parents now and groups of white and Asian and black children all played with each other – unaware that anyone in the world would ever think it was odd. Their whole lives lay ahead of them.

Night was drawing in fully now and it was the gloaming. The air became dark and the darkness laid itself upon Piccadilly Gardens as if it was its resting place. A young Spanish lady asked me if I could take a photograph of her and her friends close to the fountain with the flash of the camera on. Yes, I said, and I wanted to say yes to everything. The pace of life around me was dazzling and I was so happy that I could see again after all my years of blindness. Feeling overcome with emotion I followed the tram tracks in the direction of the art gallery and St Peter's Square. The street was quieter here and there were fewer details to grab my attention and so my thoughts retreated a little bit into my inner world and my own plans for the evening. You don't need to see anything out of the ordinary in this world. There is such beauty in everyday simplicity and there is enough happening on the streets every day to write a story or a poem.

IT'S HARD TO BE A SAINT IN THE CITY

I prepared myself in the bathroom and took off my open-necked shirt. I was about to fuck the mother of the young man who had fucked my wife last year.

Janette was in her forties and had been lonely for a while, I could tell that. She still dyed her shoulder-length hair a platinum blonde and she clearly went on a sunbed at least twice a week. I had met her on occasions in the bar that she owned and managed in the gay village. We had always seemed to get on well and liked talking about eighties pop music, which was one of her major loves. That was her decade, she told me, and the bar she owned was themed around that greedy decade. The DJs and videos on the screens always played lots of Duran Duran, Spandau Ballet and The Communards. I had an epiphany one Sunday evening when drinking there and watching the video to Bronski Beat's 'Smalltown Boy'. That video seemed to symbolise lots of the lives of young men in Manchester at the time, running away from their narrow-minded families to find solidarity and unity in the bars and clubs of Canal Street.

Janette's son Jamie worked at her bar too and he fucked my wife a few times last year. My wife Belinda doesn't think I know about it but I do. Jamie is in his early twenties and has boy band good looks – a bit of a Gary Barlow type, perhaps. Working in a busy bar and looking like that he was always bound to have plenty of success with the ladies. I reckon that this was particularly true of the gay bars in Manchester, where lots of straight women would drink to escape the sleazy men they might encounter in other parts of town and embrace a more relaxed and carefree atmosphere. Jamie definitely capitalised on this. He was always single, he once told me. I didn't talk to him much, just when ordering drinks, and I never warmed to him in any way. He seemed to have none of his mother's mischievous humour or knowledge of the world.

My marriage to Belinda had been on rocky ground for years. We married far too young and she always seemed drawn to younger men – the muscular brawny types, the ones that gave me insecurity and nightmares. I think that she had been unfaithful numerous times, but I could never get any hard evidence. Her job in sales took her all over the north of England and there were many nights spent away from home or times when she would get back to our house after I had gone to bed. My business wasn't flourishing the way that it should have and times were difficult for me after the recession. Belinda had been making more money than me for many years now and this increased my paranoia at the thoughts of cuckoldry. I hadn't fucked anyone else except her since our marriage, but she was definitely more carefree.

I first realised that she might be fucking Jamie when we both went out to Janette's bar and I noticed the two of them chatting and flirting a lot, whilst I was engrossed with other friends at a table. She tossed her hair a lot around him and

I noticed his hand on her waist on a number of occasions. I went over and grabbed her jealously and took her to the dancefloor for 'Crash' by The Primitives and we danced awkwardly and jerkily with no one else on the dance floor.

A few weeks later I read Belinda's text messages whilst she was in the shower and then I knew that they were having an affair. I said nothing and I sat and suffered for months as my business did worse and worse and Belinda and I stopped sleeping together entirely.

I was on a downward road and I knew that the only way I could change things was to do something dramatic. I thought about suicide for a while, but I couldn't decide on a method and I went off the whole idea pretty easily. Then it dawned on me that it was better to get even than to get mad. I started working out at the gym five times a week instead of two and I started taking more pride in my appearance than before – bought some trendy new clothes and got more expensive haircuts. Belinda didn't seem to notice anything different - she was still fucking Jamie the boy band lookalike - but it didn't bother me that she didn't notice my improved physique or confidence, because I was just on a mission to impress myself.

I became like Kevin Spacey in the film *American Beauty*, stimulated out of my lethargic life by my wife's affair with a younger, more handsome, stupider, Neanderthal man.

I started to listen to Bruce Springsteen's *Born In The USA* album every day.

I started going to the gym seven times a week instead of five.

I started focusing my mind on Jamie's mum, Janette, and how I was going to seduce her.

I listened to 'Cover Me', 'Working On The Highway', 'I'm On Fire', 'I'm Going Down', 'Dancing in the Dark' and 'Glory Days'. I listened to them every day and their themes and lyrics seemed to resonate with my middle-aged life. I had the soundtrack I needed to go into battle. Now all I needed to do was spend the right amount of time with Janette.

I picked a Thursday evening when I knew that Belinda was away for a few days. Thursdays are a good day to cheat on your wife for the first time – you have the whole of the weekend to recover from it emotionally and physically. I wasn't even sure that this was going to count as cheating. I knew I wasn't going to feel any guilt about it, because it was going to be an act that would give my universe some symmetry. I spent the day fiddling around at work and not getting much done. At nine o' clock I got dressed up sharp and added some aftershave as Bruce was hollering out the last lines of 'I'm Going Down' at me. Clarence Clemons' blistering saxophone solos acted as confidence boosters and team talks for the journey ahead.

I knew that Jamie wasn't working the night that I entered Janette's bar intending to fuck her. He never worked Thursdays – I had stalked him a little and studied his work pattern in the preceding weeks.

I drove into town and parked up in the free parking spaces behind the Thompsons Arms, Bruce blaring out once more:

'Hey little girl is your daddy home?

Did he go and leave you all alone?'

I let the last few lines of 'I'm On Fire' play out after parking up my car and before I turned the ignition off:

'Sometimes it's like someone took a knife baby edgy and dull and cut a six inch valley in the middle of my skull.

'At night I wake up with the sheets soaking wet and a freight train running through the middle of my head... only you... can cool my desire... uh oh oh I'm on fire...'

Janette wasn't working that night, she was just acting the hostess, but she was looking as stunning as ever. Tight ripped jeans grabbed her six-foot physique and a sparkly pink T-shirt showed off her natural athleticism.

She was surrounded by sycophants that evening and rightly so and there seemed to be a little bit of juice in every sentence that came out of her mouth. She was pleased to see me and I knew that I had a lot more to offer than the stray cats and elderly admirers that were propping up the bar that evening. Coco Louise, the well-known and well-liked Manchester transvestite, six feet tall and dazzling blonde hair, made a brief dramatic entrance before announcing to Janette that she was running a new cabaret show at the New Union on Sunday nights. Sex and religion oozed out of everything she said but she soon left and the place returned to normality again.

I could tell that Janette was impressed by my new physique and dress sense and we started talking eighties music to each other at a hundred miles an hour.

'The New Romantics were all in debt to Bowie, of course...'

We both loved Bowie, but agreed that he didn't do much great stuff after 'Let's Dance'.

'"Absolute Beginners" was his last great single of the eighties. I don't rate the *Labyrinth* soundtrack.'

'Did you ever hear *The Buddha of Suburbia* soundtrack album of the nineties?' I asked her. 'It's a lost classic.'

After a couple of hours I whisked Janette off to another bar, New York New York on Bloom Street, and we continued talking about Bowie and his enduring influence on a lot of the eighties music and fashion and style that she loved. She became sad, thinking about that decade and the impact it had had on her life and business. Inevitably we then started speaking about our crumbling marriages. Two people in their late forties saddened by the behaviour of their partners and the monotony of life around them and harking back to glory days. Janette's husband had left her five years ago and she had stayed single ever since. I spoke about Belinda's infidelity, but didn't say anything about who it was with. I felt that Janette had no clue about her son's behaviour. She didn't ever speak of him very fondly and although she knew that he lived a promiscuous bachelor lifestyle I don't think she had any idea about the actual women involved.

'So David Bowie or Bruce Springsteen?' I asked her after we had got a taxi back to my house around 2am. I really just meant it in terms of which CD she wanted me to put on as we kept talking and drinking in the living room, yet the question felt like a bigger, more epic one the moment I had finished the sentence.

'In terms of eighties output, I would pick Bruce,' Janette replied. 'He made four classic albums in that decade, all completely different and all standing the test of time. You've got *The River* – a double album about marriage and growing up; *Nebraska* – an acoustic minimalistic masterpiece; *Born In The USA* – a commercial monster that defined the decade; and then *Tunnel Of Love* – one of the all time great break-up albums, something me and you know a lot about…'

This was the kind of conversation I could never have had with Belinda. She only had a fleeting interest in music and her range and tastes were limited. She would have wanted to move this topic on quickly leaving me frustrated, yet Janette wanted to talk and talk about her eighties idols. I was relishing this kind of conversation, maybe the best foreplay I had ever experienced.

'You know that Bowie covered two Springsteen songs once,' I interjected. 'It's Hard to Be a Saint in the City' and 'Growing Up'. He knew that the man was a river of talent at an early stage of his career.

We poured through David Bowie's seventies output, agreeing that each album was a classic in its own way:

The Man Who Sold The World – dark, intense, full of sexual perversion.

Hunky Dory – poppier, quirkier homages to all his heroes.

The Rise and Fall of Ziggy Stardust and the Spiders from Mars – the decade-defining classic, but not necessarily his best album.

Aladdin Sane – dirty rock and roll and a snapshot of touring America in the seventies.

We became closer and closer on the sofa then and by the time we had reached *Diamond Dogs* we were kissing each other intensely and with no care for any of the strings that may otherwise have been attached to our lives.

As I went to the bathroom and took off my open-necked shirt and jeans in preparation to fuck Janette,

I could hear her going through my CD collection and picking the album she wanted us to fuck to. She settled on *Tunnel of Love* by Springsteen, which seemed relevant to our own disintegrated marriages. I dabbed some extra aftershave on and took a Viagra tablet whilst 'Ain't Got You' played out and then I re-entered the bedroom naked, as the first notes of 'Tougher Than the Rest' took shape. I wanted to be the character in that song, not for Belinda, but for Janette, who deserved someone tougher than the rest.

We made love in the dark for a few hours. My life felt perfect for the first time as Janette lay next to me at the end of it all.

At 6am Janette walked onto my balcony and started smoking a cigarette. I put some clothes on and joined her as the morning light started to fill up the corners of my house.

'I should go soon. Your wife may come back from her trip early and, besides, your neighbours are more likely to notice if I leave in a few hours, rather than if I let myself out now.'

'I don't want you to leave. I want you to stay.'

'Which is exactly why I have to go now,' she said coldly. 'You need to sort your marriage out first, before we do this again.'

And in a two-minute whirlwind Janette put on her clothes, gathered together her belongings, kissed me quickly on the lips and left my house. She was wearing one of my T-shirts and her platinum blonde hair was ruffled and messy in a way that I had never seen before.

After my front door closed I walked through and sat

down at my kitchen table, closed my eyes and thought about Janette's son Jamie fucking my wife as hard as he could and Belinda making the kind of noises that you hear in American porn movies. It started raining really hard against the window pane outside. There was comfort in this rain and I watched as the water created shapes and pictures against the glass for me to daydream about and keep the real morning at bay. At that moment I realised that I had experienced happiness, but that it had escaped me again and that life could not be understood at any level, but just lived through in suffering.

HOW I LOST MY MIND BUT FOUND GOD IN A LONELY BETTING SHOP

Then Satan entered Judas, called Iscariot, who was one of the twelve disciples. So Judas went off and spoke with the chief priests and the officers of the temple guard about how he could betray Jesus to them. They were pleased and offered to pay him money. Judas agreed to it and started looking for a good chance to hand Jesus over to them without the people knowing about it.

Luke 22:3–6

I got the lunch down me as quick as I could and entered the betting shop just in time for the first race at 12:50. I like William Hill and Betfred the best. I like the big screens and the sense of gambling as theatre and cinema and life and death. I knew I was gripped by it in an ungodly way. I felt like spending an afternoon in anything other than a betting shop was a waste of time. The only things that could compare were spending an afternoon in a whorehouse or writing and creating poetry and stories.

My life had little meaning by this point. The trial was a few weeks away and my bail conditions were strict – but a full English breakfast with the *Racing Post* and an afternoon in William Hill were allowed under my bail conditions. Very few other people wanted to spend time with me, so I spoke to the other betting shop inhabitants a fair bit and also to Alice, the sweet young girl who worked there every weekday. If she knew what I was on trial for I doubt that she would have been so friendly. In fact she was the only other human being I liked by this time and I wished that I could get someone like her to be an alibi, albeit a false one, for the murder that I had committed.

'How are you today, Robert?'

'Gonna clean you lot out today I reckon. Gonna go through the whole card.'

God was beyond my reach now. It was too late for any religion for me in my fortieth year. It is, I suppose, possible for a man like me to live a whole life in sin, without repentance, yet still know when you are seeing a good face, when you are seeing the kind of person that could heal you. Twenty-three years old and single and bubbly and carefree and from Oldham – Alice, the shop assistant in William Hill, was that kind of human being. She could hypnotise me in this lonely betting shop, where no one else wanted to interact with a strange man like me, with my fiery eyes and shaky hands. Men were nothing without women. Women were nothing without men. And the first race was under starter's orders and I hadn't had the chance to place a bet. The 12:50 from Worcester had been and gone in a flash and my contribution to it was nil. I needed to focus, I needed to gamble to win. Only a few weeks left until the trial now. Saint Peter had me down as a marked man and talking sweetly to Alice wasn't going to make him change his mind.

The one o'clock at Sandown Park had seven runners

and the going was good to soft. Alan King's horse was an eleven to eight favourite, but had never travelled three miles before. I liked Orchard Boy for Paul Webber at eight to one. I put a tenner on the fucker by scribbling on a blank betting slip without putting the time of the race. Alice would know, Alice would understand me, even if God and the jury didn't. I wanted to murder someone else – just to have a winner on this damp afternoon. Orchard Boy came a distant second to the jolly and four more races and four more tenners flashed by without a winner – second, third, second, third, second. I was getting a run for my money. I was getting a buzz, but no return.

An elderly female customer tried to engage me after the 2:20 at Newton Abbot:

'Kayf Tara's all need softer ground.'

What was this crazy old woman talking about?

'You keep backing horses sired by the Ascot Gold Cup winner Kayf Tara and they won't start winning until nearer Christmas, when the rains come, when the ground gets softer.'

What was this patronising crap? The whole betting shop was a mad house that afternoon. When the rains come they will all be washed away and Noah's Ark will not be able to shelter to them. Old Noah wouldn't be able to pair me with anyone. I'm not like everybody else.

I watched some more races without betting, but then focused my mind on the 3:15 at Towcester. This was the one – Prairie Town at 9-2 and I wanted to land a touch. I put one hundred on the nose and sat myself down for action.

At this point my mind drifted in and out of

consciousness. I felt alone in the betting shop and in the world. My trial was so close and God was so far away. I had been writing and writing and writing in the weeks leading up to this and some of it had juice in it and some of it was awful. Sometimes I wrote in the betting shop and sometimes in the pub nearby and Alice kept me from going completely mad by interacting with me when others looked at me like a depraved paedophile.

'Can I get you a coffee today, Robert?'

'Yeah, I need a caffeine pick-me-up. Thank you, Alice.'

She was such a sweetheart. Such beautiful green eyes to soothe and counsel me as I did my death row time.

And so on to Prairie Town. Trained by Tony Carroll. Ridden by Lee Edwards (you needed to focus hard on the jockey's first name for the shouting and explosions that could follow). A five-year-old gelding. Carrying eleven stone and eight pounds. Had lots of solid form in two mile hurdles, but running over two and a half miles for the first time. The good ground would help with any stamina doubts. Sixteen days since his last race, so should be fully fit and picked out as the likely winner by Spotlight, The Verdict and a death row writer of dubious morals and talent. I had five minutes to get my kicks.

He led from the start and jumped fluently. Turning into the home stretch and it was a three horse race. I started urging him on quietly and then louder and louder as they came down to the last.

'And it's Prairie Town and Poker School going at it neck and neck as they jump the last flight.'

There was nothing in it. Nip and tuck. The whips were up from both jockeys and I shouted and screamed to the embarrassment of all the other customers in the lonely betting shop. Only Alice smiled and had any appreciation of the adrenaline and excitement running through me. But adrenaline and excitement turned to desperation in the last fifty yards as Prairie Town faltered and was beaten a neck.

'And so Poker School takes it. Ridden by Toby Wheeler and trained by Ian Williams.'

I hurled my betting slip on the floor and stormed outside. I was £150 down for the day and it was cold and damp and gloomy and I knew no one in town and I was looking at a life sentence and Alice would never see me as any more than an entertaining customer in the afternoon.

God wasn't interested in my fate that afternoon. God wasn't interested in false accusations or the suicide of Judas Iscariot. God only concerned himself with the truth. I sank a pint of cider in the Three Swans and studied the form for the 4:00 at Worcester. I was going to put fifty quid on a three-to-one shot called Dark Flame, trained by Richard Rowe and ridden by Andrew Glassonbury, and this was going to get me back even for the day. Even for the day would mean redemption and God might look at me in a different light.

I went back inside and spoke to beautiful welcoming Alice and placed the bet.

'Fifty quid. Dark Flame please, love. This is the one. This is the one that is going to get me out of jail.'

'You going to jail soon then are you, Robert?' she laughed uncannily.

'Make sure you shout him home in your usual fashion then.'

I blew her a kiss and then went to stand in my lucky

137

spot in the middle of the shop. Together, me, God and Alice endured two dog races before the main event and I creased up my slip in anticipation as the starter got them on their way and the six novice chasers galloped down to the first fence.

> *Jesus was still speaking when Judas, one of the twelve disciples arrived. With him was a large crowd armed with swords and clubs and sent by the chief priests and the elders. The traitor had given the crowd a signal: 'The man I kiss is the one you want. Arrest him!'*
>
> *Judas went straight to Jesus and said, 'Peace be with you, Teacher,' and kissed him.*
>
> *Jesus answered, 'Be quick about it, friend!'*
>
> *Then they came up, arrested Jesus, and held him tight.*
>
> Matthew 26:47–50

Dark Flame entered the battlefield and galloped and jumped relentlessly for me as I lost my mind in religion and sex and madness. I had a comrade in the William Hill betting shop that afternoon, another man my age, less mad perhaps, less desperate, who was also willing Dark Flame on over every fence on the big theatrical screen and our unity seemed to make Dark Flame run faster and he led by five lengths running down to the last fence.

To be level again at close of play was the one glorious aim. To have some dignity and not to betray myself or anyone and to not feel like I needed to kill myself on my walk home. As Dark Flame ran down to the last fence with an unassailable lead I walked out of the betting shop and onto the street. I was going to do some writing and I was going to do some creating. I had to fill the time somehow until my trial. Alice would be there again for me tomorrow, as would the English breakfast and the next day's *Racing Post* and a flurry of exciting horse races to help pass my scared afternoons. I could find out if Dark Flame had won when I entered the betting shop again tomorrow lunchtime. Borrowed time is the best. Not knowing the truth is beautiful. I had not yet decided in my own head whether I was beyond redemption or not.

Rimbaud had his absinthe, Johnny Cash had his pills. Give me a collection of fast racehorses every day of the week.

SUNDAY MORNING AND SATURDAY NIGHT

Manchester has everything except a beach.

Ian Brown

The best Saturday nights out are the ones where unpredictable things happen and where all the members of your group have their own separate crazy adventures that they can share with delight by Sunday lunchtime. The best nights also hit you unexpectedly. Anticipation has the habit of setting you up for disappointment in the long run.

There wasn't much build up to this particular Saturday night. The plan initially was just to go to the Morrissey disco at the Star and Garter on Store Street. The beautiful Polish barmaid Anita would be working and me and a few mates could get drunk and jump around to our favourite indie tunes. I got Terry and Dave out too. The three of us could drink at my flat on Pollard Street first and then head down there around eleven. We each got a six pack in and some food. What else was there to do in Manchester on a November evening when it was getting dark at five o'clock? After the excitement of the football results coming in we all had a long slog ahead to get through to Monday morning and the lectures that we were all supposed to attend. So there we were, three twenty-year-old single likely lads, drinking beer, putting our evening shirts on, applying too much gel onto our hair and listening to the Strokes, the Smiths and the Libertines. We had a sense of unity as the night started to build up. We got along just singing our song; if people told us we were wrong, fuck 'em.

We wanted to create some romance, inject some magic into the air. Terry, our natural leader, the best-looking one out of us and the most successful with the girls, set the tone for the evening with a spirited team talk around ten o'clock that injected some menace into the air.

'Lads, there ain't no romance out there.'

'What do you mean, Terry?'

'I mean, people are saying that there aren't any great causes left to fight for. That our generation is just too into mobile phones and the internet and buying clothes. Well they are wrong – there is a camaraderie to three single lads like us going out on the pull. We can make some magic happen tonight. Come on lads, drink up. Here is to the likely lads of Manchester and the adventures that lie ahead for us tonight. Anything could happen tonight…'

Terry was a working-class Mancunian from Middleton and he dressed the part. He had the swagger and the Liam Gallagher phrases and mannerisms. He slept with a lot of girls, but he didn't want any of them to get too close to him. He liked his own bedroom just to himself at least five nights a week. He was studying media and journalism and was considering sports journalism as a career when he graduated. He was a huge Manchester United fan and was in good spirits because of his teams three–one thumping of Swansea that afternoon.

141

Dave was Terry's best mate. Red-haired and also from Middleton. They had grown up together and their families were close. Yet Dave was clearly the follower in the relationship. He would follow Terry in trends and music and fashion. He lacked Terry's charisma and good looks, but he was a reliable and likeable guy.

I had known both of them for around two years, having met them in my first year at university. I was the outsider from the group I guess, because I was from Nottingham and a Nottingham Forest fan. I didn't have any Mancunian swagger, but I knew my indie rock and roll and I could outdrink both of them on a night out. With the girls I was hit and miss. Confident and successful some nights and nervous and edgy on others. I needed to drink a lot to get anywhere and I had never had a proper girlfriend or had sex sober.

We headed to the Star and Garter and got served by Anita. We drank a few and jumped around to 'First of the Gang to Die' and 'Everyday Is Like Sunday'. But Terry was restless by half twelve.

'There are no girls in here for us tonight, lads.'

'Yeah, and none of us are going to get anywhere with Anita,' Dave remarked. 'Even though she is probably perfect. She is working all night and will have to clear up until five.'

'Yeah, fuck that.'

I had had five beers and a vodka coke and felt like taking the lead.

'Let's all jump in a taxi and head to The Venue – it will be more lively than this. Cheap vodka Red Bulls and it is Dirty Dancefloors night.'

We went out onto Store Street and boldly walked north. We passed two streetwalkers and gave them each a turn of phrase. They both looked like they had pimps and had been pushed into what they were doing. I wondered for a few seconds about what had gone wrong with their lives to need to be selling their bodies on a cold, dark, damp November street after midnight.

'I'm sorry, love. I will have to turn you down.'

We jumped in a taxi. The red light indicated that the doors were secure. Our taxi driver seemed to want to talk to us as much as possible on the way there.

'We want to go to The Venue please, mate,' Terry shouted.

'Yeah, just off Deansgate,' I added.

I wanted to be the leader tonight. Fuck Terry and the fact that he had always led his gang all his life. I was going to take over tonight. I was the outsider with a cause. I wanted to do something memorable. Something that all of us would remember and talk about for years to come. And I wanted to steal Terry's thunder.

'You three boys gonna pull in there tonight then?' the taxi driver asked us on our journey.

'Hoping so, mate. We want to meet some rock and roll girls,' I shouted back at him.

'You got your dancing shoes on then?'

'Oh, yes.'

'It's lock up your daughters time,' mused Dave unconvincingly and the three of us exited our taxi and joined the queue to get into the nightclub. The queue was longer than we expected. The Star and Garter had been a bit dead, but The Venue was the complete opposite –

a long queue and lots of students spilling out across the street and smoking and posing and posturing.

The queue started moving down gradually. I had made up my mind that the moment we got in there I was going to buy six double vodka red bulls. We could all neck the first one to make up for any momentum lost in the taxi and then enjoy the second one. They were green in colour and sickly sweet in flavour. Maybe we should just down the second one too actually and just enjoy the effects and the music and the fact that we were alive.

Terry started chatting up a few girls in the queue in front of us, a standard procedure for him on a night out. Dave observed in admiration as he always did. He had all the lines and all the moves. Any impartial observer would have noticed that he was acting like a dickhead to mask his own insecurities, but it genuinely seemed that the three girls in front of us, with their rock and roll T-shirts and pale northern complexions, were loving it. I didn't want to get involved; it all seemed frivolous and Terry's fake braggadocio was starting to really annoy me, as was Dave's pussy-whipped attitude. I had bigger fish to fry and I wanted to do something legendary tonight.

I started staring hard at the two bouncers in front of me. One of them looked alright. One of them looked scary and was going to give as many of the lads trouble as possible. I focused so hard on looking normal and sober that I started to worry that my manner might seemed contrived, that I might come across like I was completely hammered, but trying hard to impress.

It was OK though, I got past the bouncers. We all did. We paid to get in and ran with elation down the stairs, burst through the doors of perception and each punched the air as we made our way to the bar.

'Six double vodka red bulls please.'

They were slimy green, worse than I had remembered from previous experiences.

We necked the first three to a toast of the three musketeers.

Against the will of the other two I created a huddle and a toast to 'Manchester girls' and insisted on necking the next three.

Plastic glasses on heads.

Crumpled plastic glasses squeezed in my hand and thrown on the floor.

'Your round, Terry!'

I had unnerved the great man and was throwing down a challenge to him that he hadn't anticipated.

I walked past the ten thousand eyes in a line, over to the wall where the heights of different famous rock stars are measured. Having been nervous and uncertain with the girls in the queue, and any other attractive females that I had encountered that week, I now swooped in and started talking to a red-haired girl about my age, stood with a few of her friends at the end of the bar.

'Let's see which rock star you are?'

'How do you mean?'

And I took her over to the rock stars wall. At that moment Terry brought the next round over and I instinctively grabbed the double vodka and red bull out of his hand, necked it and threw the plastic glass on the floor. I focused on the red-haired girl.

'Sorry, I didn't catch your name…'

'It's Sophie.'

I fancied her with a passion. She was a Topshop princess. A rock star too. She had control over my eyes.

'Sophie, my dear… tonight you are…' I measured her up on the wall. 'Tonight, you are Debbie Harry.'

She laughed and smiled and spoke softly, 'Oh, I love Blondie.'

'And I am… Joey Ramone.'

This was perfect and led us on to a great discussion about New York and punk rock and our respective musical tastes. Three great topics to start up a conversation with a girl. I was in full flow now and easily out battling Terry and Dave, who were trying to talk to Sophie's two friends. Out of the corner of my eye it was looking uneasy and as if the conversation wasn't really flowing. I didn't care. I was in the zone now. I thrust a twenty pound note into Dave's hands and told him to get six double vodka Red Bulls in. He would have been too gormless to grab the initiative himself.

The conversation flowed and flowed. We drank our next round, and feeling like I was flying, I took Sophie, my Manchester girl, onto the dirty dancefloor. We went straight to the middle of the club and threw our bodies into frenzied shapes.

We made eyes at each other.

She was like an explosion.

Dancing like a robot.

I didn't want to kiss her yet, though. I wanted her to really want me. I told her how beautiful her green eyes were and then took her off to the other side of the bar, away from her friends and my friends.

I was really in full flow now and talking about Robin Hood and Elliott Ness and Sydney Carton. All the good guys and the outlaws and how some people were both and how some people were one of the two and if you were neither, you didn't count. I think Sophie said she was studying English literature and media studies and she was enjoying my literary conversations and comparisons. She said something to me about Anthony Burgess and we drank some shots and another vodka red bull. She probably couldn't see for the lights but she kept staring straight at me (when I spoke). If it wasn't so dark she might have seen how red my face had become.

Manchester girls.

I am going to do something legendary tonight.

And Terry is nowhere to be seen and not able to cramp my style and wreck my advances, like he had done so many times before.

We went onto the dancefloor again.

And The Smiths played 'Bigmouth Strikes Again'.

And James played 'Laid'.

And Oasis played 'Don't Look Back in Anger'.

And the swirling mists surrounded us.

And I felt amazing. Better than I had ever felt before.

And the swirling mists surrounded me.

And I was going to do something legendary.

I woke up in a hospital bed and my stomach had been pumped. It was very bright and I felt that there was so much white around me that I could have been in heaven and surrounded by angels. I asked one of the angels where Sophie was and they didn't respond. I reached over for my phone out of my trousers, which appeared to be on an empty bed next to me. I flicked through all the contacts and Sophie was nowhere on my phone.

Two missed calls from Terry.

Two missed calls and a caring and concerned voicemail from Dave.

They were probably both tucked up in bed at their house still.

My phone said that the time was 8:15am

Sunday morning was not as great as Saturday night.

I had no recollection of anything after 'Don't Look Back in Anger'. Had I done anything legendary? I don't think I had. Or if I did I didn't remember it.

After a while a doctor spoke to me:

'I think someone had a bit too much to drink last night. Too much for your age anyway.'

'I am sorry,' my mind replied. 'Is there a certain age you are supposed to be?'

And I was free from the gang now and I at least felt proud about that. Once I had recovered I would need to re-enact that Saturday night. Again and again. Again and again, at least until I turned forty. And I needed to find Sophie. What Sophie and I had talked about at the bar last night made so much sense.

GET OUT OF LONDON

I stepped off the train onto the platform at Euston Station and I instantly felt like I was surrounded by vultures and vampires. I had immersed myself in that day's *Guardian* on my way down. There were warning signs but I was oblivious to them. I was conscious of passing through Milton Keynes Central, but this didn't stir me. As my feet hit the grey tarmac on the platform I realised I was an intruder. How could I get across the city as quickly as possible and down to Brighton? When was the next train back to Manchester? They left London Euston every twenty minutes, right?

My life had enough love and poetry and beauty in it. I didn't need to do this. Why had I decided to come down to London anyway? I pulled down my shirt and looked at the Lincoln green Robin Hood tax tattoo on my left shoulder that represented a world where truth and justice might one day reign. I felt like a traitor.

No one was talking to one another.

No one was smiling.

Everyone was preparing for the Underground.

Everyone was thinking about making more money.

I was going to see more homeless people than I could handle.

I was going to see a bigger gap between rich and poor than I could handle.

And I was going to see the naked evidence of the forces that exacerbated those divides. The public school faces. The public school red faces. The public school haircuts. Around me people were reading *The Financial Times* and fingering their oyster cards. I stepped in terror into the main part of Euston Station. I was barged out the way by the ugliest attractive young woman I had seen in a while and hassled by the pushing and shoving of the evening commuters. I didn't want to go outside to the brothels and the sex shops. I didn't want a lousy burger in The Rocket or the prospect of treading the place of my watershed debacle all those years ago.

I could see no evidence of anything immortal down here. No evidence of any sense of revolution. The largest billboards seemed frozen and full of the word 'preparing'. *Time Out* magazine seemed unfamiliar and distant. All my energy and enthusiasm for life was draining away from me rapidly as I stood surrounded by the whirlwind. I was scared for my own future. I was scared for everyone's future.

Outside, Eddie Rocket's and Nando's and Pret A Manger were spilling over with angry faces that had lost Jesus and didn't want to find him again in a rush. I respected Charles Dickens, but I felt like his idiot child today.

I stood statuesque in the vortex and called God a liar.

I remembered the 7/7 bombings and Live 8 and the week it was announced that London had won the Olympics again, but I felt no connection. And I started thinking about

Hiroshima in 1945 and the bombing of Dresden and the plights of aboriginals and Native American communities and the way that history can conceal the biggest lies and create the wrong heroes and never even tell us about the anti-heroes.

This is not my world, Boris Johnson.

This is not my world, Sebastian Coe.

This is not my world where everyone is trying too hard to get higher up the ladder.

I found my return ticket and returned to platform 2. The next train to Manchester was leaving in five minutes.

And everything looked the same as it always did.

And the men checking our tickets looked prompt and heinous.

And I boarded and found my own table.

And two friendly ladies came and joined me.

One looked like a barmaid.

The other looked like a stripper.

And I started breathing normally again.

At least I was aware that my panic attack had not been visible to anyone.

And I closed my eyes and said a prayer for the lost magic.

I felt the gentle tug of the train moving and closed my eyes and smiled.

'This train will be stopping at Stoke-on-Trent, Macclesfield, Stockport and Manchester Piccadilly.'

THE UGLY ONES

All that really matters is what is inside that can of beans. It doesn't matter what the packaging is like. It doesn't matter how much the can costs. It doesn't matter what counter you got it from. It doesn't matter whether you got it from Sainsbury's, Tesco's or Waitrose. All that really matters is what is 'inside' that can of beans.

Liam Gallagher

Anthea was an only child and grew up closer to her dad than her mum. Anthea's dad was a real man's man; he had been a gangster in his youth and owned a villa in Marbella. He loved to watch mafia and gangster underworld films and would stay up late watching them with his daughter after his wife had gone to bed. By the time she had turned twenty you would have thought that Anthea would have wanted a man that resembled her dad – a hard man, with big muscles and tattoos and a cold-blooded attitude to life. However, as much as she loved her dad, she actually wanted something totally different.

Anthea was a peroxide blonde and wore a lot of make-up. She claimed that men in bars and nightclubs never came and chatted her up because they were intimidated by her. She had a strange and voluptuous body and had worked as a stripper in her first year of university to make extra money. She never told her mum or her dad about this, but she told me straightaway.

Anthea's spirit was usually high and positive and she had an infectious energy about her. Many people thought she was a bit crazy. A lot of the boys her age thought she looked like a slut and talked derogatively about her behind her back. None of them wanted her as a girlfriend because they knew that their family or friends would mock them – she wore too much make-up, she looked too 'easy', she wasn't the kind of girl you brought home.

Anthea struggled to make friends with other girls her age. They tended to make bitchy remarks about her and none of them thought she was pretty. She brought out a condescending and sanctimonious attitude in other girls because she was so carefree and uncomplicated. There was no pretence with Anthea, and I noticed that straight away. In some ways I think that people were jealous of her. She cared deeply for other people and animals and she felt intense pain and sorrow when she saw anyone or anything getting hurt. I guess that this cruel world was only going to be a fleeting resting place for Anthea, before she became overcome with the suffering she saw around her and her inability to change it all.

I must have been one of the uglier guys in town on the night when I first met her. I was in my thirties, out of shape and hadn't washed for a few days. Any chiselled looks I may have had in my twenties had faded into a double chin and soporific, wounded eyes. I didn't believe in love either. I thought the whole thing was a charade – narcissism for the insecure and people that couldn't be alone. I walked into the pub that night alone and wanting to be alone, because I knew that I could write well on my own and see the world with unblinkered and unaffected eyes.

I was trying to write some poetry and didn't notice Anthea at first. The pub was fairly busy and there was a humming sound around me. I was in the zone, trying to put my last few days into some kind of rigid verse. Anthea later told me that she had been staring at me for a while before she came over and spoke to me. She was drawn to the ugly ones and the ones who made no effort with their appearances. The people that she was with that night were only half-acquaintances.

'Can I buy you a drink?' she asked me.

I was stunned out of my keyboard. This approach had never happened to me before. At first I thought she was like a vision of how Jayne Mansfield from *The Girl Can't Help It* would have looked in the twenty-first century.

'Only if you are having one too.'

'Sure.'

We smiled at each other. It was the first smile I had allowed onto my face all day.

'Let's get doubles then and I am buying,' she went on before I had any chance to place an order.

'Double Jack Daniels and coke?'

I nodded obediently. I was the ugliest guy in the pub, both inside and out, and I didn't believe in love, so I was happy for her to take the lead.

When she came back from the bar we introduced ourselves properly and talked about what had brought us to the Black Lion that night. She explained that she was dropping out of university and working full-time in a mental health hospital. I told her I was a writer and trying to get a book published, but having my struggles with writer's block and inspiration. She analysed that part of me closer than anyone had done before and I could feel my writer's block dissipating as I became captivated by her movements and expressions. She had chosen me and there was nothing I could do about it. There was nothing I wanted to do about it.

'Do you think I am ugly?' I asked her after we had been talking for half an hour.

'Yeah,' she replied. 'Do you think I am ugly too?'

I stared at her and didn't answer straightaway. I thought for a while about how this strange creature would want me to answer this question.

'No, I don't, but there is something else. There is a loneliness in you that I think we both share. And I can feel that beauty right now.'

'My dad is a gangster,' she went on. 'Do you know about the Manchester gangs?'

'A little bit,' I shrugged.

'He was in the Quality Street Gang with the Noonans. He did some awful things to people. But he never got done by the law. He is still a free man. I am his only daughter and we love each other in a way that my mother doesn't understand. All that he wants to do now is to protect me. There is so much violence and suffering in the world and we are all so powerless to do anything about it, don't you think?'

I didn't answer Anthea's question. I just wanted to know more about her relationship with her mother. I knew that I was going to write a story about this girl as soon as I could. Her half-acquaintances had left the pub now and the two of us settled in with some more drinks.

'My mum is the classic gangster's wife. She was drawn in by the money and the glamour at first. Like the wives in *Goodfellas*. But she is powerless to change my dad's ways. She is jealous of me because I am the apple of my dad's eye. I can change him. I want to change him and I have done. But my mum can't stand the power I have over him. The power that she has never had. And it makes her want me as far away from home as possible. I guess that is one of the reasons I am in this pub talking to you tonight.'

Anthea laughed loudly and then grabbed hold of both my hands.

'I like the fact that you are a writer and that you have come in here on your own. Will you base one of the characters in one of your stories on me?'

I told her I would.

'I also like the fact that you think you are ugly. Beauty is nothing. Beauty doesn't last. Me and you are both lucky that we are not beautiful, because it means that when people like us, they really like us for what is inside and not for what is on the surface. Can I go home with you tonight?'

We went back to mine that night and we stayed up talking until 4am. I discussed the stories and the poetry that I was writing. I told her that I was looking for truth in everyday scenes that busy people normally glossed over – things like homelessness, emptiness, depression and death. But I wanted the truth in them to be beautiful and prophetic and help people (and myself) to make more sense out of life. She spoke more about her parents and then about past lovers. She had never found a guy that she wanted to settle with, she told me. At first no guys matched up to the confidence and charisma of her dad, but in the last year she also saw that no guys actually understood her. Men wanted to own her, she felt, and this wasn't what she wanted. She wanted to be free.

As we fell asleep, we both turned away from each other and there was no sexual chemistry.

In the morning we woke up and turned towards each other.

'You are the only man who hasn't tried to have sex with me when we have shared a bed.'

I told her that I thought she was beautiful, but that I wanted to see her again and for her not to just be a one-night stand. I was telling the truth and she really liked that.

Anthea went into my bathroom and freshened up. She had to leave for her job at the mental health hospital, she told me. She came out of the bathroom with a fresh layer of make-up on and her long peroxide blonde hair flowing down to the bottom of her back. Her eyes sparkled in my direction and before she turned to open the door and leave my flat, she started kissing me, slowly at first and then faster and with a lot of tongue.

'See you later, lover man.'

And she turned and opened the door and left for her day at work.

I wasn't working that week and I slept in until midday every day. I would have a shower and then go to the café at the bottom of my road and read the papers and eat a bacon and egg barm. I would read in the afternoon and get ideas for writing. Sometimes the ideas flowed and I made notes in the margins. Sometimes the ideas didn't flow and I thought about Anthea and when I would see her again. She was impossible to forget.

I saw Anthea next at the weekend and she told me she wanted me to take her either greyhound racing or to a boxing match. These were the things that she used to do with her dad growing up, but he had tired of it now apparently and she wanted to go with me instead.

'Bring your notepad and pen with you,' she told me. 'And remember that there is truth and beauty at all of these working-class meetings.'

And so I took her to Belle Vue and we had a great time and we won a packet of money and went out on the town to celebrate.

'So are you interested in my body or my mind?' Anthea asked me later in the evening after we had spent most of our winnings.

'I am interested in both,' I told her. 'Your body has a great rhythm and poetic motion to it. And your mind is so original and unaffected by custom and stereotyping.'

We both seemed happy at my answer and that night we went back to my flat and made love for the first time. We looked into each other's eyes throughout the experience and slept in each other's sweaty bodies afterwards, without needing to towel off or shower or go to the bathroom.

The next week I drove south to spend some time with my family and to make a visit to my publisher, who was looking at ways to hype up my latest collection of short stories. I told Anthea that I probably wouldn't be able to see her for a week.

When I returned to Manchester, Anthea didn't answer any of my calls. I was stressed about this for a few days and then I let it lie and got on with my ugly life as usual. Sitting in the corners of pubs with my laptop, observing people out on the street and their robotic motions – painting them like Lowry, but with bleak and sparse sentences.

Anthea's disappearance and absence from my life haunted me for months and months. Why was she not answering my calls? Was there something I had done to upset her at some point? Had something happened unexpectedly with her family that had caused her to leave the city? Other than her phone number I had no other way of getting in touch. I scoured Facebook, but couldn't find her. She seemed gone from me forever. All I could do was replace her in my life with Jayne Mansfield and watch *The Girl Can't Help It* over and over again.

It was over a year later that I saw the headline on my newsfeed and there was the picture of her face:

MANCHESTER GANGSTER'S DAUGHTER COMMITS SUICIDE

Anthea had overdosed on pills a few days after her father had been convicted of drugs and murder-related crimes going back fifteen years with Salford's notorious Quality Street Gang. The article said that the girl's closeness to her father had led her to getting involved with criminal activities on his behalf and ultimately perverting the course of justice. If she hadn't killed herself she was likely facing a trial and a potential prison sentence of up to ten years. Her father was still alive, but it looked likely now that he would spend the rest of his days in Strangeways prison. The picture of him was blown up next to a smaller one of Anthea. He looked really ugly and mean and old – exactly how you imagine a notorious criminal gang member looking. In comparison Anthea looked angelic and sweet and innocent. There was, however, a slight similarity in their mouths – both looked tough and cold as if they didn't invite or want kissing.

As I finished reading the article, whilst stood by the newsstand on the corner of Cross Street and Market Street, I could tell that the newsstand owner was about to tell me that I had to buy the paper if I wanted to keep reading it. That sense of impending tension was combined with the pervasive sound of pneumatic drills all around me, as construction workers put together the new tram tracks that would make the city a fairer place to live in.

Anthea had been a good person. Too good for this world and too good for the forces surrounding her. I looked to the sky and yelled out:

'GOD DAMN YOU! WHY DIDN'T YOU TAKE ME INSTEAD?! YOU COULD HAVE HAD ME INSTEAD!'

The pneumatic drilling became louder and I knew that no one was listening and that there was nothing I could do to change what had happened.

MANCHESTER IS A POEM DISGUISED AS A CITY

Ask the saints and sinners
Ask the angel-headed hipsters
Ask the beggars, the boozers and the madmen
They will all tell you that Manchester is a poem disguised
as a city

Ask the drag queens on Canal Street
Ask the homeless in their communities on Oxford Road
Ask the Alan Turing statue on Sackville Gardens
They will all tell you that Manchester is a poem disguised
as a city

Ask the people of the People's History Museum
Ask Deborah Curtis, Tony Wilson and Peter Saville
Ask the Sex Pistols at the Lesser Free Trade Hall
They will all tell you that Manchester is a poem disguised
as a city

Manchester is a city where God moonlights naked

KILLER ON THE LOOSE

There is a killer on the loose
She has an almost perfect body
Sways in the sun as she walks
Down The Avenue in Spinningfields
With her poodle and Gucci bag
Tanned long seductive legs
And hips you would want to grab hold of all night

She won't get her credit card out for world poverty
She will get it out for more plastic surgery
Or hair extensions and those sharp long nails

The girl with long black wavy hair confuses me
More than the other men
That she runs to and from each week
Offering up endearments
Telling them she loves them
Then leaving violently
And breaking their naïve or innocent spirits
The younger men especially

But not an old man like me
An all-night drug prowling wolf
Who can share the same street as her
And the same moonlight as her
And not get killed like the others

A HEDGE FUND BANKER

A hedge fund banker
A soulless corporate wanker

Here he is
Walking out of St. Paul's station
Never had a hangover
Never stopped for a Big Issue *seller*
Never stopped for a charity fundraiser
Never had a decent blow job
Or a spontaneous threesome
Never hung out in the bookies
Never got drunk in a northern city
Never wanted to kill himself
Never been in love

Sons go to the right schools
Holidays in Cornwall and the south of France
Wife goes to the right social occasions
Whilst fucking the gardener
In the garden shed on Friday afternoons

Only God knows
If he will get into heaven.

MY DEATH

My death
Will not make the front pages
Or the back pages
Or any pages
There is no loyalty
No one will cry when I am gone
My funeral will be small
They say you die twice
Once when you draw your last breath
And again when the last person who knew you dies
It won't be long from one to the other
For me

I should have been a man of the sea
And commanded my own pirate ship
And seen shipwrecks and skeletal sea creatures
And Moorish walled cities
And lived by the sword
With my own harem of Sally Browns
And raped and pillaged
And burned and drank and fucked
Like each day on the rolling sea
Could have been my last
Instead today is my last day

I am waiting to die
Just like I was waiting to live
Waiting
Waiting
Waiting is the loneliest verb
In the English language

JOE STRUMMER IS ALIVE AND WELL AND LIVING IN MY HEAD

Joe Strummer is alive and well and living in my head in
Manchester
Just in case you were wondering
I thought I would reassure you all
In case any of you had lost hope

He can still crawl through a festival way out west
He can still think about love and the acid test
He can find a little drop of poison
To inspire a fireman or two to strike

It is the first of November tomorrow
And American election day draws ominously near
A night when I will stay up and not go to bed
For Castro is the colour that will earn you a spray of lead
In times like these we need his rebel spirit more than ever
But don't worry
Just in case you were wondering
Joe Strummer is alive and well and living in my head

167

ROBIN HOOD BLOOD SISTER

No dice son
No dice son
It ain't gonna happen
There will be no justice tonight
Truth will not come out this time
And so

And so I surrender to the rain
I surrender to the Manchester rain
It is like an old friend
And I will go and find a girl with a record machine
White noise
When it comes to rocking she is a queen
At least when she comes out of jail anyway

I will put on my lonesome raincoat
I talk to you a lot in my head
Can you hear that?
Robin Hood Blood Sister
Your fire will change the world
And you are a catalyst to your disciples
Spring into action for me please
And I will stay in love
With a girl locked up in a jail somewhere
Until I go to jail myself

PIN YOUR HEART TO THE MAST OF A SHIP

The Clash are the only band that matter
John Cooper Clarke is the only poet
Manchester is the only city
Horse racing is the only sport
Alcohol is the only drug
Trainspotting *is the only film*
Fundraising is the only job
Charles Bukowski is the only writer
You are the only girl for me

Pin your heart
Pin your heart wearily
Pin your lonesome heart wearily
To the mast of a pirate ship
And set sail across the rolling sea
To the Americas
To the New World
To New Zealand
And don't ever look back, my friend
I will meet you on the shore
And be ready to raise hell with you

A LITTLE BIT OF JUICE

I need a little bit of juice in each line
To keep me turning the pages
So that I can justify my literary interests
I like Kureishi, Kesey and Kerouac
I feel no juice in James Joyce

If you want to know who your real friends are
Go get yourself a false rape allegation
And watch the bastards turn their backs on you

You've got to give it all you've got
Or just forget about it
YOU've got to give it all you've got
Or just forget about it
You've GOT to give it all you've got
Or just forget about it
You've got to give it ALL you've got
Or just forget about it

This could mean alienating all your friends
This could mean ruining your body
This could mean totally neglecting your health
This could mean becoming homeless
This could mean being a single person forever
This could mean social rejection
This could mean being blocked or deleted off social media
This could mean going to jail
This could mean getting beaten up in jail
This could mean an ugly old age
This could mean a painful death
But you have to stick to your guns

You have to give it all you've got or forget about it
Because it could lead to a magnificent nirvana

Do not trade in half measures.

HERE'S TO THE NUTJOBS

I keep falling for all these crazy girls
The damaged and bipolar ones
I have known mad women, addicts, whores and suicide girls
I love their spontaneity and sense of adventure
And I want to cure and rescue them
Just the same way as I want to rescue everyone I can

I see happy couples walking down Oxford Road
On dreary Morrissey Sunday afternoons
And I feel like Mark E. Smith
Popping into the Lass O'Gowrie
To romanticise about a telltale heart

Here's to the nutjobs
The crazies and the women that will drive you to the edge
Of insanity, alcoholism and pill popping
I become addicted to their games and the chase
And the chase is better than the catch
For me
The catch is stultifying brownstone
Like New York before the Ramones

I see the happy couples in supermarkets
In IKEA waiting for their new bed of growth
I see many men with quiet and sensible girls with money and
   careers

Here's to the artists
The penniless, the mentally ravaged animals
Who raise money for charity
Or give out soup to the homeless
After tearing up the dancehalls and underground nightclub
   floors

Give me a nutjob
From a broken family
And pink or blue hair
And original fairy tattoos
And I will fall in love with her forever
For my close friends all know
That a good woman scares the hell out of me
Like my bathroom mirror reflection on a Monday morning

MADNESS SETS IN

It comes at you like a freight train
When you least expect it
And your equilibrium falters
I have tired eyes
From teenage highs
I am Robin with no Batman
A sidekick with no hero
My own worst enemy
I am in love with my weakness
I am red today
Madness sets in

Substances have eroded my calm
History has chosen me like a messiah
It is time to go
But the ocean doesn't want me today
Am I bleeding?
Second hand stigmata
I am a velvet rope
Michael Hutchence's last minutes
I am the fairy tale
Both hunter and hunted
The digital display of an alarm clock

But I want to stay here
To stay addicted to the head fuck
Drowning in wine
I promise you I am fine
Madness sets in

WHEN IS THE REVOLUTION COMING?

When is the revolution coming?
Punk rock leather-clad girl
When is the revolution coming?
Robin Hood Blood Sister
Ripped jeans and spikey-haired seductress
I am ready
Ready for the revolution when you are

There is a revolution coming
I will fight with you or alone
I am not waiting for recognition
I am not waiting for verbal ammunition

I am a rock and I speak for myself
I wasn't made for these times
And I am not like everybody else
I am riding the bullet train
On a journey straight to your heart

I am begging for change
My brother, my sister
My son, my daughter
If you make that monumental jump with me
If you take that leap of faith
Revolution may happen now

START ALL OVER AGAIN

It is the thirty-second of December
And once again I awake to the pressures of new resolutions
My body starts to shake
Sending a vibration
Across this nation
People seem old
I feel cold
Plagiarism is ripe
I am the Noel Gallagher of punk poetry

People take the easy way out
With drugs and alcohol
They are overly proud
About their once-a-year success
As the smoke signal ascends
To universal foes and friends
For some kind of solution
To this one's New Year's resolution
That makes no sense
No more
No less
In undeniable repulsion I digress

Once more you flunk it, you fake it
And January rolls on
The September Man you had seen has gone
And on and on and on and on and on and on
Your charity has already been paid for
And in thirty-nine years
With blood, sweat and tears
You take a new approach, a new view
And maybe there is a chance, for a new you.

TATTOO LOVE

Gonna get lots and lots and lots of tattoos
Some of them drawn by you
My tattoo girl
My tattoos will never be as great as yours
For sure

My voluptuous ripped-jean-northern-indie rock and roller
Lover of Joy Division
Angel of The Smiths
Tattooed and pierced
Painted and punctured
Denim, metallic ink
Green and blue
Black and brown
Pint of cider in one hand
Book of poetry in the other
Your mouthfuls dislodge illicit imagery
And forbidden worlds

She leaves me naked and alone
And is gone too quick to understand
I run out and look around
I see nothing

And back to my bed, damp with our sweat, Louise
And the drinks we spilled with our frantic lovemaking
'I can't tell anyone about this'
'I can't ever do this again'
This is the price you have to pay
For tattoo love

OUTSIDER BLUES

It's better to be on the outside than on the inside
Pretend you are in a war if you can
It's better to be on the outside than on the inside
To live outside the law you must read sonnets

Give me a tale of mystery and imagination
And let me go and find the Veedon Fleece
Through the streets of Arklow
I have searched and searched and searched

It's better to be on the outside than on the inside
Whatever people say that my personality is, that is what I
  am not
It's better to be on the outside than on the inside
Everyone else don't pull no punches
Only outsiders know how to push the river
As long as they are universal in sympathy
The Veedon Fleece is theirs

It's better to be on the outside than on the inside tonight

YEAR ZERO

Year Zero was a good year to be born
The future wasn't unwritten before it.
From Year Zero onwards
The rockabilly thing ain't working out
For all the good old boys
Especially for Snakehips Dudanski
And the black mountain poets

I value my existence by what I create
Creation is everything
I am the philosophy
I am the engine
I am punk rock
Without me there is nothing.

The Punk Rock Warlord has the keys to your heart
He has left the Windsor Castle days
The best frontman out there
Descending from Scottish heather
And Woody Guthrie
Bound for glory

We can all do this together
Rehearsal rehearsal rehearsal rehearsals
Passion is a fashion
We can all do this together
We can stop kids joining up to the National Front
Out of ignorance
We can all do this together
Lock me in a prison cell with you for three days
And drop the act

The future is unwritten now

YOU SHOULD NEVER FEEL ABOVE ANYONE

You should never feel above anyone
The audience are your friends
You have got more ideas in a rhyming couplet
Than I will have in an entire lifetime

You should never feel above anyone
The men on the street have integrity
They may have served in a war you were never called up for
They may have experienced a double whammy you will never
  know

You should never feel above anyone
People younger than you are your friends
People more junior than you are your friends
What does it really mean to be free?
Hate cannot drive out hate
Only love can do that
You should never feel above anyone

SANDINISTA

I have been running and running from the police
I was running August
Running with the September Man holding me back
Running October

But I found my true voice
In a Nicaraguan-themed city centre bar
Where there is a truth in the attack
There is a romance in seeing the city like this

Does this man deserve to be in jail?
Like the Sandinistas
And the People's Liberation struggles
I need to redress the lack of inspiration
That used to exist in my body and soul

I am having a nervous breakdown
The police are on my back
And I am running November
Running December
Running January
Running

HOMELESS ON DEANSGATE

There is an old man standing on Deansgate
He stands there every day
With his ghetto blaster loud
Not asking for money
Just begging for sympathy

Sometimes I see him in betting shop doorways
What would he be without his music?
I have heard him play 'Under Pressure'
And the 'Woodpecker from Mars'
I keep seeing him

It must be a rough life
Homeless on Deansgate
No one understands
No one shows any emotion for him
I have more time on my hands now
So I watch him and he watches me
And we understand each other

He is lost with that ghetto blaster
I am lost without one

ELEVEN LINE POEM

It fucks you up two thousand and sixteen
A year with a hex on it
A year gone rogue
I didn't expect it to but it has
David Bowie died at the start of the year
Because he knew how bad it was going to be
We lost Muhammad Ali, Leonard Cohen and Prince
Endured Brexit, Trump and a loss to Iceland
They say that nothing is lost
In the satanic mills and underground clubs
They are wrong this time and I am too

ONE CHAPTER LEFT

I look at a reflection of myself
The wind of change has blown through me
Too apathetic for suicide now
Imagining myself elderly and in a home

'There is so much to look forward to today…'

'Um, yeah, if you say so.'

I have one chapter left
Maybe just to climb a magnificent mountain with you
But I am aging faster now
I am bloodless, ambition gone, maverick gone

'Isn't it a lovely day, Mr Dalgety?'

'Um, yeah, if you say so.'

Two young punks walk by me and sneer
Excited by power chords and skirts
That used to be my world
But was I ever that carefree and that bold

'You should really come outside into the garden now.'

'Um, yeah, if you say so.'
The garden of middle-aged dross holds nothing for me
I am not ready for the last chapter yet.

BETTER OFF WITHOUT A GIRLFRIEND

A girlfriend arrived in my life one day
Without me anticipating or predicting it
A bullet to my head
She messaged me constantly
Hourly banal life updates

I couldn't be friends with other girls
I spent less time with old friends
Had bad nights of sleep
Entered a world of jealousy and arguments
And suddenly I can't do what I want to do every day

She fixed my phone (or so she said)
She organised my living room
She made me file my bank statements
And throw away old postcards and letters
And do a savage Facebook cull

I felt better when I had my disorder
Gonna take a few weeks to get back to normal now
I have lost my rhythm
And been robbed of my dishevelled spontaneous life!

TEN LINE POEM

The rush of energy I felt last night
From my turbulent brain
To my inspired fingertips
Made me think I could write my magnificent octopus
But the adrenaline was fleeting
And I adjourned the meeting
Back to normality
Alas, I am fine
The city of the damned had drowned and disappeared
By the end of the tenth line

LIVING IN THE NORTH

I much prefer living in the North of England
London is full of condescension and over-bloated egos
And suits and bankers and wankers
Give me Manchester, Liverpool or Leeds any day
There is camaraderie and my kind of politics
That establishes longing and belonging
When a person dwells in the North

In the dead of morning
As the young sun rises
I see the youthful spirit of the Beatles and Arctic Monkeys
And I want to stay up North for the food and the hills
And the girls, who speak their mind freely

Here is the story of the new geography of England
Climb Kinder Scout or Scafell Pike
Drink cheaply in indie rock and roll bars and clubs
Whilst the southerners keep trying to climb the social ladder
And spend one eighth of their life
In impersonal silence on the Tube
Trying to figure out how they can get ahead
As their spirit and soul become dead

Let it rain on me up North
No Chandler's Ford for me
No Clifton Triangle
No Stoke Newington
Or Ealing Broadway
Maghull loves me like a rock
Headingley is my endless youth
Salford is the dirty old town of my dreams
I am going to stay up North until I die
Until the Spanish and the French and the Americans
See that London and the home counties
Are telling them a whopping lie.

MANCHESTER IS A CITY WHERE GOD MOONLIGHTS NAKED

There is a young man sat outside the Thirsty Scholar on
Oxford Road
Sometimes the student girls sit and talk to him when they are
drunk
But he knows more about life than they will ever know
My girl sat and talked to him once because she cared about
others
Manchester is a city where God rides naked

The young man whistles down the wind
And looks like Jesus Christ at times
Alone and persecuted
The world ignoring his pain and message for now
But my girl sees it and tells me all about it

Invisible cars and magic buses fly by him on Oxford Road
The intellectual conversations are few and far between
Sometimes for a change or a quieter day
He sits outside the Lass O'Gowrie
And he knows more about pain than we will ever know

My girl wants to help him and so do I
We go together to find him
After a lunch at Joshua Brooks
But the site of the Calvary Cross is not an open invitation
He is gone today
I need to find my own pain
I need to confront my own demons
For Manchester is a city where God moonlights naked

FUTURE WIFE

She put her number in my phone as Siobhan Future Wife
We even discussed the details of the marriage
The first drunken night we met in Mojos
Our affair faded fast and now she dates rock stars
Male models and professional footballers

I am walking down Cross Street
And I see her walking towards me with two other girls
Dressed in tight blue jeans
I watch her contours waving
And she looks directly through me
My creased leather jacket like a bulletproof vest
On on on to the next one

I walk up to Fopp Records
And lose my afternoon
To the sounds of Ian Curtis and Joy Division
And bands that sound like Joy Division

OUTCAST

They don't talk to me any more
Those fake plastic friends who are scared of the law
'I never really knew you,' they say
'It's up to the courts to decide'
And I stand in silence with my mouth open wide
And stare at the pavement I once trod with confidence

One false accusation and I am gone
One person's lies and so many desert me
Then I am reminded
I need to see it from all angles

Write about your own personal experiences
Write about the life that you know
To make it through this life I must be universal in sympathy
   and understanding
Yet an outcast and a rebel by nature

FIFTEEN-YEAR-OLD BOY LISTENING TO LED ZEPPELIN

A fifteen-year-old boy listening to Led Zeppelin albums
I think that was the happiest time I can ever remember
The poetry and the mystery and the album covers
Believing that the 'Battle of Evermore' was real
A real story for a virgin's brain

Religion was fading and sex was only a hint
As the young girls climbed up the Giant's Causeway
Well before the vodka and the tequila entered my veins
It's been a long time
It's been a long lonely time
Just as it was before then

I walked as if rhythm had never been invented then
Through green fields and dark woods and coppices
With my black dog and a tangerine
At the bottom of a Christmas stocking
This was a new world for me
'The Rain Song' seemed better than all the classical music in
    the universe
The pleasures of the damned

Available always to protect and ensure
That actually there would be no loss of innocence
Not for many years now

A fifteen-year-old boy listening to Led Zeppelin albums
Was a mountaintop time for me

THE DEAD SOULS

A London estate agent from Foxtons
And his girlfriend who pretended to do something good
Because he provided her with enough money and security
From safety to where?

They went to Center Parcs for their holidays
Like dead souls
It was like a luxury ocean liner
Full of the rich and the indolent

Both treading safe paths
That their parents and safe friends approve of
Listening to Adele albums and the 1975 (when adventurous)
Getting married soon and thinking about a timeshare
Yet they don't share their time with anyone
Too different from them

Center Parcs is like a floating tomb
With dead souls everywhere
Treading safe paths
With their credit card lives
I am staring at the shiny cocktail couple
And I want to throw up on them

These are the souls of the floating dead

BAWLERS, BRAWLERS AND BASTARDS

Hey you!
I like a little drop of poison in my world
Don't tell me I drink too much
Or that I need to expand my range of interests
And explore more wholesome activities
I don't need The September Man right now

I like binge drinking, gambling on horses and chasing after girls
I like stuff which is low-down to help me stay
Young at heart
I have got drunk and brutally honest
In practically every town in England

I always kiss like it is my first kiss
I always drink like it is my last night
And my bank account is empty
I can relate to the prisoners now
Whose cause was better
Who were poor but not deluded
Who Johnny Cash sang about
And Tom Waits held dear.

Hey you,
Whether you like it or not
I am going to live through it and dance through it all
For the sweet poetry of redemption.

PASTMASTERS

I saw Johnny Lightning the other day on Chapel Street
In his creased leather jacket and on his motorbike
He had just come back from riding with angels
Through the promised lands
On an epic road trip adventure
To hearts and empires of darkness and back to the light

He had been to the place where Buddy Holly died
In February 1959
The exact field where the plane came down he told me
He had been to the piece of road
That was Eddie Cochrane's last, so they say
In 1960 when touring England
With Gene Vincent
(Why oh why did Elvis never tour England?)

Johnny Lightning's road trip had taken him
All across the states of America
Lynyrd Skynyrd's Free Bird bar in Jacksonville
And the great honky-tonk saloons of Nashville, Tennessee
And back across the sceptred isle
In the Cavern where the Beatles played
To Rehearsal Rehearsals and the Albion Rooms of London Town

But Johnny had come back home now
And he wanted to talk to me
And me alone
For longer than my other female friends would have predicted
It was worth writing a poem about
Johnny.

GIRL IN THE CHARITY T-SHIRT

There was a pretty girl raising money for a charity
Standing in isolation on Market Street yesterday
Her T-shirt was a bright colour
And on the back was a slogan I couldn't ignore
'Until There's a Home for Everyone'

And I wanted to wear that T-shirt too
And stand alongside her
So that together we could show the world
And the cynics and the critics and the apathetic
That Until There's a Home for Everyone
We live our lives in a horror show – a bastard motherfucker
    world.

FREE FROM THE PORN INDUSTRY NOW

Louise has got her shit together now
She is free for the first time in her life
Away from the drugs and the bad parents
She is free from the porn industry now

Louise was once a big-time adult movie star
You might have seen one of her scenes
Renowned for anal and gangbangs
But Jack wasn't good to her at all

She has got a big apartment of her own now
She works afternoons in a school
Has her own business
And helps out at the sexual health clinic
Does yoga
Has become a vegetarian
And has a new boyfriend that is studying medicine

Despite the new interests and habits
Louise is still the same carefree fun-loving girl
That she started out being on camera
But she got out at just the right time
And didn't get infected with HIV
Or hooked on the wrong drugs
Or manipulated away from her real personality

205

With her long black hair flowing down her back
As she strides to her yoga class
I wonder what has happened to Jack
He probably doesn't know what he is missing out on.

GUTS

This poem is a 'fuck you'
From your favourite T-girl Coco Louise
To the people who think
A person can only really be successful
If
They push themselves to the very brink
Possibly to madness
Possibly close to death
Method living
They would say
But have never actually had the
Guts
To try doing something like that themselves.

NEVER HAD NOBODY NEVER

I wake up at ten
I get out of bed at eleven
I crack open a can of cider for my breakfast
I had been running wild with some new contacts
No one who really cared that much
But they had a gallant rebellious charm
That reminded me of better times
I played with them
And I fought with my aging physique
I had a wild old time as I remember

I crashed into my flat at four
And nursed self-inflicted wounds
And tried to fight off the dawn
That was determined to get me
Like a tide
Inevitably drowning a man half buried
On a deserted winter beach

The dawn had won the battle
And I spent the afternoon watching Trainspotting
For the fifty-seventh time
I feel like Morrissey in the eighties
I never had nobody never

SITTING IN ST ANN'S SQUARE AND
THINKING ABOUT WHO I AM GOING TO KILL

I really need someone to help me out
I wish that someone would sweep down onto St Ann's Square today
Uptight, uptight
Please don't leave me on the backburner

I have followed God to this dark and lonely place
I became radicalised but chose not to join ISIS
I need to find my own way of making my mark though
Paradise and multiple virgins await me
If I can find the strength now
Like the statue looking down on me
St Ann's Church behind me
And a fountain and busker ahead

Who shall I kill first?
The man guarding the jeweller's shop
Looks loveless and ripe for my vengeance
Or I could pick a younger shop assistant
At the Office shoe shop
She has clearly never contemplated God

There is a loneliness in this world so great

That you can see it in the slow movement of an autumn leaf
Falling from a tree in the rising wind
The loneliness is in the pavement
The loneliness is in the water in the fountain
The loneliness is in the rejection of the busker
The loneliness is in the rejection of The Big Issue *seller*

No laughter or tears on St Ann's Square today
I want to wield by bayonet
I want to unleash myself on this world
Unannounced at first
And mutilate and maim
Thoughtcrime does not entail death
Thoughtcrime is death

But for now I watch the leaves falling
And the fountain flowing for tomorrow
Tomorrow could bring a better mood in me

THE HUG

The leaves kept on falling on St Ann's Square
Autumn's short-lived gloaming was nearing
I walked across the square trying to keep my anonymity
By looking at the sky above
Not noticing the freaks and lovers

As a wanted man I put my hood up
Yet there she is with a group of co-workers
We get eye contact
How will she react to the malicious lie about me?
Whose side has she taken?

I shuffle over
I don't want a big funeral when I die
I want to be forgotten quickly, I think
But as we get nearer
Her face lights up
One of the most beautiful radiant smiles I have ever seen
And she gives me
The biggest tightest most heartfelt hug I have experienced in a
    long time
The great hug tells me all I need to know
And life is worth living again

FREEDOM FIGHTER

They say that one man's terrorist
Is another man's freedom fighter
And I am both of these for sure
And my own chemical ingredient too

I killed for my children
I killed for their freedom
I killed to set the world on fire again
For you
Reading these lines

I just want the sullen darkness now
A grave that is like this night
An undiluted grave that I deserve
Deep, perfect and undiscovered
I believe in myself at this moment
There is nothing else to believe.

MORE POETRY

To be writing more poetry
At the age of thirty-nine
To fill up my empty days
Like a schoolboy with no pressures
In the summer of 1990
When England reached the semi-finals of the World Cup
Scorching hot days and nights.

Surely I must be crazy now
To be doing it all over again
Twenty-six years later
Betting shops and alcohol and fervour now
Dirty laundry piling up
Winter nights drawing in
Nothing to fill my time with
No future
No future

Keep writing more and more and more poetry
To keep myself alive one day at a time.

MY FRIEND CHARLOTTE

My friend Charlotte
Has hair like Tina Turner
Looks good in her 'Who the fuck is Mick Jagger?' T-shirt.
Like a vampire she
Comes alive in the night time
Starts revolutions in Cuba
Tests her boss's patience
Starts riots as a tequila queen
A midnight fire starter
She has always been

My friend Charlotte paints the autumn nights
With daytime stripes and colours
Jumps through happiness
Might be going to Australia one day to pay her dues
But for now she is chasing after Barney the barman
And keeps me from getting the blues

FOREST 'TIL I DIE

Down the back roads of West Bridgford
I glide on my magic bike
This pocket of the world is just like heaven
I imagine I was living here in '77
The year the dream caught fire
The year that the explosions started

I wouldn't say I was the best manager in the country
But I am in the top one
Who do you think you are?
Brian Howard Clough
Just a statue in the Market Square now
A relic of the city like, Robin Hood
Alan Sillitoe and now Jake Bugg
Keeps some of the fire alive
Oh so lonesome on my one

I am back home as I glide through the grey city streets
On my one
I am Forest 'til I die
In a Manchester dream I had last night

A WILDERNESS OF PAIN

Alone now and soon to die
In an interview I can talk the truth
This is the strangest life I have ever known
Most people lack the imagination to suffer
As I have
In my twenty-seven years

Let's drive to the beach tonight
Sit under a moonlight drive
With all the city madmen and the bums
That represent my community tonight

I am going to die soon, my friend
Rock and roll is the sound of angels telling the truth
Not mine
Not my brand of rock and roll
Rock and roll is the sound of angels telling us all beautiful lies
Beautiful, resplendent and highly addictive lies
As I walk through The Doors into the dirty nightclub

RUNNING WITH FIRE

Paris 1924
Brave men and foolish men
Had set sail for ultimate glory
Across the tombstone of the sea

Persecuted for being a Jew
I had just ten seconds to justify my whole existence
And I won
And we won, the human race
I have never yet known contentment
Always chasing chasing
Even after Paris I kept chasing
And it kept me hungry
In the North of England

I am an addict for chasing
I am an addict for running
I am an addict for life itself
It's a weapon I can use

I have known the fear of losing
But now as an old man
I am almost too frightened to win

Keep chasing
Keep chasing

A FABULOUS YELLOW ROMAN CANDLE

Old Dean
Is like young Dean
More beautiful
Less sexual
Still burns burns burns
For kicks kicks kicks

A third of his time in the public library
To question all of existence
A third of his time in the pool hall
To handcuff the other beatniks around him
A third of his time in prison
The only place where a man can really be honest

In the darkness as an old man
He is still able to talk to his disciples
The mad to live
The mad to die
And like you
The mad to be saved
It gives me comfort to know
That in old age
Both of our fires have not yet gone out.

THE BEST MEN

It struck me today
Whilst eating my tarama and bread
In Café Istanbul on Bridge Street
As two men fought outside
On the autumn pavements
That some of the worst men in the world
Have some of the best jobs
Like Donald Trump
So lacking in manners and integrity
Yet some of the best men in the world
Have some of the worst jobs
Because they refuse to compromise
And choose principlism over pragmatism
Until they become
Outcasts
Outsiders
Unemployed
On the streets
Or in the asylums

I know I need to help these men somehow
And fight some kind of battle
With others

Or alone (if needs be)
For the soul of humanity

I am in pain now and my skull is cracking
Post-traumatic stress disorder from the war
There are ghostly voices in my head
I could be a counsellor by day
And write grotesque novels at night
For no greatness in this world comes
Without a dance with death

A MURDERER

I saw him arrive at my parents' house
In his public school tweed and sporting attire
Talking of adventures and flippant deaths
He seemed to smile all the time
Whilst telling his horrific tales
Elvis Costello would have had an acidic opinion of him
He wouldn't last long in a Salford pub

I never smiled back at him once
I tried to avoid his company

He kept taking great pride in his appearance
And tucked in both his shirt and tie
Showing off a shiny belt with a Latin crest
Polished shoes and a polished life
The Army first then the City, naturally

I did not like his life
I did not like him

He charmed the ladies with wealthy tales
And racist jokes and contrived etiquette
'A better class of person'

He said a number of times
And I left the house and got into my car

I drove around the country lanes all night
Listening to the songs of Woody Guthrie
And some early Leadbelly
At high volume
Whilst driving slow
The rest of the evening
Reminded me of what I want to fight for and against

A POET'S LIFE

You have to walk around all day on your own
Kicking yellow leaves through autumn pavements
And observe observe observe
All that you see
The obvious
The absurd
The sad
The beautiful
The alcoholics
The prostitutes
And the prostitutes in suits
And the buskers
And the movements of the clock
The daily lives of madmen
And robotic witches
And all the seasons of the heart
And all the paces and moods of the streets you see
And the sentences we hear without thinking
And the words we read without questioning
Question everything
And get drunk regularly
And write drunk
And write sober

And write sober about writing drunk
And write drunk about writing sober
And gamble when you can
And break up witch trials
And keep it all to yourself
And don't try to impress women
Don't try to impress anyone
Bring all you see to life
And write it all down
And never edit anything
And don't let your publisher edit anything
Or try and convince you to ever edit anything

If you do this
The city holds all you need
For all your life
And if you hit the keys hard
I hit the keys hard
You can write hard ballads
And honest poetry

LIKE A SUICIDE BOMBER IN DRAG

Passing the time waiting for the investigation to end
Passing the time playing marbles
Passing the time losing your marbles
Passing the time in dark corners of pubs
Passing time in betting shops
Passing time writing short stories
Passing time writing immortal poems

Passing the time waiting to be a free man again
Passing the time like a machine gun singing
Passing the time learning to play the drums
Passing the time reading the gospels
Passing the time reading Maupassant
Passing the time reading the Bard of Salford
Passing the time listening to Joy Division

Passing the time hoping the police know what the fuck they
   are doing
Passing the time watching pornography
Passing the time reading about rape
Passing the time thinking about love and death
Passing the time walking the streets naked
Passing the time dripping into a bucket of blood

Passing the time sleeping, getting lost, circling the whole
  fucking planet
And coming up roses
Like a suicide bomber in drag
Who changed his mind twice

ADVICE TO A YOUNGER INDIE KID

You should listen to more seventies stuff
Buzzcocks, Undertones, Joy Division
The Clash, The Jam, The Ramones
And stop posing and preening every day
And get yourself into an unhappy love affair
And experience deep unrequited love
And go all the way
Go. All. The. Way

Binge drink more on a Friday and Saturday
And only date girls with interesting tattoos
Don't talk about anarchism or nihilism
But practice socialism
And vote and go to rallies and get out on the street
And do a job you really give a shit about
And only spend time with people you really give a shit about
Or just be alone
And create every day
And go all the way
Go. All. The. Way

Listen to reggae and folk and ska
And buy music you can hold
And talk and listen to people in record shops

And book shops
And betting shops
And date foreign girls
And read One Flew Over the Cuckoo's Nest
And Brighton Rock
And Uncut *magazine instead of the* NME
And go all the way
Go. All. The. Way

Ignore labels and DJs
It is only the music that matters
And play your musical instrument
Or don't play your musical instrument
And create acidic poetry for people with learning difficulties
And stand up for the disabled and the old and the young and
  the poor
And shed your racist friends forever
And shed your materialistic friends forever
And go all the way
Go. All. The. Way.

THE SUBTERRANEAN

O deep thinker you
Did the Beat writers light up a spark
Of spontaneous thought
And spontaneous prose
And just being a bit more spontaneous with your motherfuckin'
  life?

If you are on the road to insanity
Like The Boy In The Bubble
Like Robert Walser
They will put your little ramble
Into One Hundred of the Finest Short Stories Ever Written
That glimpse of truth
Is inside you subterranean...

When you are in the drunk tank
They might call you a genius then
And posthumously you will get the credit
Like Van Gogh
Or Nick Drake

I think I would like to be posthumously famous
But I haven't got the patience.

EVEN IT UP

She stands out on the street and strives
She works to inspire and to change
The Robin Hood tax and my Robin Hood blood sister
Can make the world a fairer place
Shake people out of their apathy
Get out on the street and even it up

She builds rapport and improvises lines
She hits the target every time

She fundraises for forgiveness
Forgiveness of her fears
She fundraises for understanding
Understanding of herself
She fundraises for recognition
Her work is a protest
She stands a cappella on her own two feet
She would fundraise for free
But sometimes she fundraises for me

Get out on the street and even it up!

TWENTY THINGS YOU SHOULD HAVE TOLD ME

I want you

I need you

I love you

I miss you

Sometimes my whole body and brain ache for you

Like a storm trooper I will guard your soul

Life is shorter than you think

Death is just around the corner

The sex was fulfilling

Only breathe into my mouth

When I left that night I cried

I pity you

Baby please don't go

I can't say goodbye

I eat all men alive

I don't love you

I have changed

There were no other men

Like John the Baptist I am preparing you for your greatest prolonged pain

I wish we could start all over again

WISDOM COURAGE PATIENCE

I went to see the Archbishop of Canterbury last night
With my mother
At the Cheese and Grain
In Frome town

Surrounded by lots of churchgoing folk
He told of how he used to work in the oil industry
I wasn't convinced by his comments on gay marriage
I wanted more conviction
I wanted him to come out in favour of it
But he sat on the fence

However, on my life he was helpful
Wisdom, Courage and Patience
He told me
Wisdom to act correctly
Courage to confront my demons
Patience to know that the truth will come out in the end

I guess that is why he is the Archbishop of Canterbury
I drove my car up to the River Irwell
Sat alone by the water
Watching for a rip tide
And the last glimpses of sunset
Caressing the water in front of me
And set out my manifesto

GRAVEYARD GIRL

I saw the graveyard girl again today near Chorlton Meadows
She must be seventeen
And just finishing college
She whistles old pop songs
And occasionally sings Jim Morrison lines
In a soft falsetto

I saw the graveyard girl today
And she saw me for the first time
We exchanged a long expressionless stare
And then she floated on
With her magic fluid movement
And whistles and songs
Past the headstones
And the church she never entered

I can tell she is alone in this world
Waiting for someone to love her meanly
And destroy her innocence and magic
Whilst I dug graves
And slept in graves
Like Woody Mellor before he was famous.

MISS MANCHESTER IRISH, YOU ARE A LADY

I had to leave Manchester
And go to Ireland to live a little
To write and get inspired
Sometimes I feel so uninspired…

I didn't take MacGowan's boat train
But talked in waves
To my driver from the airport
As we headed to the Camden Street end of town

She told me that she was forty-four
And built like a rock chick
Born the year Thin Lizzy released Whiskey in the Jar
Celibate for six years now
I didn't want to alter this
Or alter her emerald spirit in any way

We could hang out in Leitrim
Play or write poems in the rain
And pretend to be Oscar Wilde for a day
We can drink the dark stuff
And wander down to the Long Hall
But when you are gone I will feel lonely
And you will go back to your Queensrÿche

And We Are Sexual Perverts
And I will go back to my fucked up life in Manchester again
Which I escaped for six hours with you yesterday

THROW IT OFF THE BACK OF A TRAIN

You can take all of your titles
All of your posh friends
And your father's connections
And your debutante balls
And your tweed jackets
And your striped shirts
And your stiff upper lips
And your casual racism
And your inherent snobbery
And your Henley Regattas
And your Royal Ascots
And your fear of the North
And your fear of activism
And your fear of change
And throw it off the back of a train

You can take all of your old boy's clubs
And your King's Road nightclubs
And your Made in Chelsea *friends*
And your Bullingdon Clubs
And your Riot Clubs
And your grandfathers and fathers
And your military connections
Killing human beings

And your City connections
Killing human beings
And your tax avoidance
Killing human beings
And your subscription to The Spectator
And your disdain for Jeremy Corbyn
And your safety blankets
Never jumping out of your bubble
Believing you are better than everyone else different to you
Killing human beings
But making people like me stronger
To tear down your false worlds and gods
And radicalising me
To actually change things
And make life better
*For the humble and the kind and the loving and the salt of the
     earth*
Who aren't killing human beings

You can take all of this now
*Before the sun sets on the city that has everything except a
     beach*
And throw it off the back of a train.

NORTHERN QUARTER HOTEL

The white sunlight devours my bedroom
The blinds seem to have no purpose
Except to make her blind to me now

I am the bastard son
Of Molly Malone
And the lonely ranger at Clontarf Castle
As you escape your convent girl background
Your Catholicism and your rosaries
To go down on me one more time in the morning

As you pile your belongings together
To leave me like yesterday's man
In the Northern Quarter hotel
Above buskers
With the Thunder Road café calling me
And the loneliness of the day calling me
I kiss and caress your back
Knowing that this is the last of our affair

We are delivered an Indian summer
Just when we think our time is up
And then autumn cascades in with all its power
And I know for certain
That she doesn't love me.

DON'T TAKE LIFE TOO SERIOUSLY

Don't take life too seriously
None of us will make it out alive
Alan Turing didn't
Ian Curtis didn't
Tony Wilson didn't
Myra Hindley didn't
And they didn't have mobile phones either
Or Facebook
Or Instagram
Or Twitter accounts
But their stories will last for centuries
Don't take life too seriously
None of us will make it out alive.

GETHSEMANE

For you I sing with a body electric
Like good old Walt Whitman
For you I would hold back a nation's tears
For you I can be humble or proud on demand
For you I have waited all these years

For you wherever you now are
I walk through the valley of my soul
For you in silence at Gethsemane
I whisper darkly my selfish goal

Musicians have written songs for you, I pursue them
Artists have painted in agony, I cry for them
Yet your eyelids stay closed and refrain
From ever knowing that electricity
Which can show all my love in a heartbeat
Only you can kill all this pain

I AM DOING THE BEST I CAN

Why don't you sing
'I am doing the best I can'
Maybe even get it as a tattoo

It doesn't matter if we are out of tune
Because you are cool

My average relationship lasts three months
With arguments
Inflation
Coercion
Festivals
Other girls
Writer's block
Gambling
Lonerism
I am doing the best I can

I like sitting on my own in pubs and reading books
I like loud northern girls with black-rimmed glasses
I like shouting home the winner in a two mile chase
I like playing air guitar and dropping to my knees

I can handle being alone in this world
I want to be alone for now

Sex repulses me right now
I don't want to thrust
I don't want to enjoy foreplay
I don't want to change positions
I don't want to be on dating apps
I dislike myself at these times
Feeling nothing
Going nowhere

I like my compact disc box sets
The Pogues, Johnny Cash and Thin Lizzy

I want there to be a knock on the door
Right now
And I want you to be stood there alone

ONE WILD HOUR

Come with me
I want to spend just one hour with you
One hour of madness and happiness
We can play staring competitions
Dance to Maurice Williams and The Zodiacs
Cut each other beautifully
And make a lifelong blood oath

We will create lightning and thunder together
And the old lady below may hear
And the gossiping groups may interpret
Our acts as signs that we have both finally
Finally, lost it completely
As they had been expecting and cynically predicting

Let's make this hour now
You and I alone
We can drink from mystic glasses
Deeper than the rest
And be savage and tender
Away from ties and conventions
We will escape utterly from chains and claws
We will run dangerously side by side
Loving freely
And talking recklessly
Forever
About the one wild hour we spent together

Come with me now

MASS OF CONTRADICTIONS

You feel like my muse right now
As I receive your letters by airmail
You who are an addictive Mass of Contradictions
Dolly, Biff, Rebel Rebel, Anna Karenina

I have realised today that our best friend in the whole world
Is the open road in front of us
As we hit the accelerator and turn the music up loud
And I trust in you now
Robin Hood blood sister

I am excited by the road ahead
This road expresses me better than I can express myself
If you come with me
We can meet the indigenous souls and absorb them into us
The people of Fiji, Samoa, Tonga or Vanuatu?
Can share this fast-paced trip

It could be a white knuckle ride, high octane
Far removed from the Tiger Lounge and the Satanic Mills
I think you can put your troubles behind you (and I can too)
And drink and eat and sleep
At one with the vibrations of the earth beneath that big smile

Let's do it!
Come travel with me!
Don't let the waters around you become too calm
Don't throw your anchor out yet, you are too young
Forget your money and ties for a while
And surrender to an act of rebellion
I am not offering a twenty-first-century traveller's experience
No Lonely Planet *or Full Moon Parties here*
I am envisaging a journey of self-discovery
For the Let's Go Crazy Tottenham Hotspur girl
Will you come travel with an old man
And contribute a powerful new verse
To the song I am trying to sing?

WAITING FOR THE POLICE TO CALL

Monday thirtieth of January
Sitting in my flat on my own
And waiting for the police to call
And listening to Joy Division

Texting my friends
Pacing around the wooden floors
Wandering onto the balcony
Staring into the mysterious lugubrious grey sky
Who is up there watching me?
And waiting for the police to call
And listening to Joy Division

All outcomes still possible
My fate in a police officer's mind
Listening to Digital
Listening to Transmission
Listening to Atmosphere
Listening to No Love Lost
Thinking about the nightmare I have lived through already
And the one that could be to come

Staring at that grey Manchester January sky
Still and perfect and quiet
And pacing those wooden floors again
And waiting for the police to call
And listening to Joy Division

THE LION INSIDE ME

There is a lion inside me
And he will reveal himself soon
Just hang on a bit longer February
Build up all your strength
And prepare
For the rest of 2017

There is a lion inside me
King of the jungle
All swagger and mojo
Hibernating now
But waiting to dance free
In the rest of 2017

There is a Mancunian lion inside me
That has experienced pain recently
But is healing
And calculatedly knows
That the best is yet to come
In the rest of 2017 and beyond.

APPENDIX

Four characters make recurring appearances throughout the book and act as motifs for some of the themes and experiences that run throughout:

THE SEPTEMBER MAN – aging and wise. A Manchester sage with plenty of raw life experience and cynicism. He doesn't believe in love, only experience, and encourages other characters to think like him.

ROBIN HOOD BLOOD SISTER – a beautiful young Manchester punk girl with short hair, strong opinions and an altruistic left-wing desire to change the world. Wears Ramones T-shirts. Never wears Guns 'n' Roses T-shirts.

COCO LOUISE – a blonde, six-foot-tall Manchester transvestite. Obsessed with Marilyn Monroe and trying to escape a harsh loveless working-class upbringing. Equally obsessed with sex and religion and having as much of both in her life at the same time.

THE BOY IN THE BUBBLE – a shy student-aged black boy with a speech impediment and an overactive imagination that takes him into dream worlds with dead sports stars, rock stars and literary icons. His likeable and easygoing character brings out the best in people and enables normally feuding characters to get along. Like Kurt Vonnegut's Billy Pilgrim, he has the ability to travel through time.